Beyond Digital Transformation

Advancing Tech for Accelerated Growth

Nana Fifield

Technics Publications

115 Linda Vista
Sedona, AZ 86336 USA
https://www.TechnicsPub.com

Edited by Emily Daw
Cover design by Lorena Molinari

First Printing 2021

ISBN, print ed.9781634629416
ISBN, Kindle ed.9781634629423
ISBN, ePub ed.9781634629430
ISBN, PDF ed.9781634629447

Library of Congress Control Number: 2021939478

To my parents, Professor Robert and Rosemary Ampomah, my role models, intelligent, talented, inspiring academics.

To my sons, Luke and Paul—my amazing heroes.

And to my brothers, Yaw and Robert.

I would like to sincerely thank Steve Hoberman and his team at Technics Publications for making this book possible. With his guidance and mentorship, his patience and direction, this book was able to come to fruition.

And finally, acknowledgement to Jeremy Posner, my friend and supporter, without whom I would not have started this journey.

About the Author

Nana Fifield (neé Ampomah), MSc, BEng, is a senior technology leader, an engineer, and a certified Agile transformation agent with a career spanning almost thirty years in the technology industry. Her educational qualifications include a Bachelor of Engineering degree in Electrical Engineering and a Master's degree in Digital Systems. Since the early 1990s, she has worked at several well-known corporations, including IBM, Digital Equipment Corp, Nortel, BNP Paribas, the Sage Group, Rockwell Collins aviation, and Depop. She has also collaborated with organizations such as Google in building technology communities. Nana was voted as a finalist in the Leadership category of the 2018 Precious Awards, which recognizes successful and inspiring women of color.

Over the past decade, the author has transformed engineering teams for small, medium, and large organizations, at local and global scales, across multiple geographies. She has worked closely with business leaders, CTOs, CEOs to drive rapid change and led global innovation programs to support growth in new markets.

The experiences and lessons she gained over the years helped her realize the need for transformation across the technology industry. Delivering business value through software projects is complex and less understood. The learned patterns and practices collected over many years led the author to write this book - how organizations can mature their technology practices to deliver faster and win more customers as they build their trusted brand.

Nana lives in Berkshire, England, with her two wonderful sons.

Contents

Introduction

The world is at the cusp of The Fifth Industrial Revolution — an age defined by a mature technology industry.

Technology is by no means a modern-day phenomenon. Technology has existed since prehistoric times, and the term itself has origins in the Greek concept of a "science of craft." It was originally concerned with the skills and methods of practical subjects such as manufacturing and craftsmanship. With the emergence of the Second Industrial Revolution and over the last 200 years, technology has risen to prominence and has taken on new meanings.

There is a distinction between science, engineering, and technology as we understand it today. Science is the systematic *knowledge* of the physical or material world gained through observation and experimentation, and engineering is the *process of designing and creating* machines, systems, and tools. This leads to technology, which applies the outcomes obtained from both science and engineering, which means that it involves the techniques, skills, methods, and processes used in producing goods or services.

Despite the evolutionary pace of technological change, the modern technology, or "tech," industry is relatively immature. In this book, we will explore the characteristics of industrial growth and maturity by looking at the lessons learned over the past two centuries through the series of industrial revolutions. Each stage represented a significant technological shift and acceleration based on the learnings and foundations of the previous. Industries have grown and evolved through experiences from each revolution, enabling them to transform to become today's mature and established markets. However, this has taken decades and, in some cases, centuries in the making.

Why is maturity desirable for any industry? Mature industries have well-defined standards that serve to address the expectations of their market in a way that is broadly consistent across the industry. This is partly due to businesses that have grown, survived by obtaining a significant edge over their competitors and have a well-established market share based on their brand, reputation, and service levels. Having built credibility over the years, they are seen as generally trusted and stable with the ability to retain their competitive advantage. Through cycles of change and efficiency improvements, their profit margins and earnings improved, as they continued to accumulate cash while at the same time providing more capacity to evolve. This has given them a strong position to reinvest in high growth opportunities to boost revenues and wealth.

The capability of a business to mature within its industry is the subject of maturity models. Several models have been devised with well-defined characteristics at each stage to measure a business to assess maturity more formally. The benefit of maturity models is that they can provide standardized definitions and pathways to help organizations develop their own capabilities through their people, operations, practices, and technologies as they grow. An industry-standard benchmark helps them understand their position against their competitors. As customers, it provides the ability, through trusted definitions, to make comparisons between different suppliers on a more level playing field to determine whether they can deliver the desired value.

This book revisits the lessons of the past to identify the patterns and practices that have been defined and adapted, and provide a learning platform for the technology industry, currently in its relative infancy. This approach will uncover methods to apply for accelerated transformation across the technology industry.

The first part of this book will look at those lessons gained from the early industrial revolutions. Subsequent sections will address the challenges facing the technology industry and how these lessons can be applied to help accelerate the industry's momentum to achieve greater advancement.

Chapter 1

Industrial Growth and Maturity

Industries arise out of new demands from a variety of sources. Innovations and technological breakthroughs, entrepreneurial activities, consumer demand, as well as environmental, economic, or natural events contribute to industrial formation in one way or another. An industry can enjoy decades of sustained growth with evolving products and services, leading inevitably to the challenges it will face, whether due to competition, trade, or technological advancement. While some industries die or become obsolete, most evolve to meet new conditions of demand.

All industries go through similar lifecycle stages of introduction, growth, maturity, and decline.

At the startup or introduction stage, a unique product or service innovation is created and aimed at a selection of early adopters. Efforts are focused on education and driving awareness of the product while investing in its development. In the growth stage, with increased marketing investment, demand starts to accelerate due to a surge of consumer awareness, and new companies enter the market. As a result, competition intensifies and product entries to the industry become more standardized. The industry eventually matures, with growth slowing and larger companies retaining greater market share and dominating the industry. Consequently, opportunities for new or small companies to enter the industry decline. Although sales continue to grow, the rate has declined, with cost reduction, market share, and profitability being the primary objectives.

Eventually, the industry may reach the stage of decline when the products become outdated or are superseded by newer innovations. Demand is negligible, and sales are in decline with fewer companies competing for the smaller market share. Some industries have continued to grow through reinvention and expansion either by entering global regions, repurposing existing offerings or creating new products.

The modern world has experienced multiple industrial revolutions, each bringing a set of technologies that have paved the way to a new direction in human society. Industrial revolutions are characterized by technological advances in some form that advance human life.

Several industries have lasted for many decades and some for centuries, evolving over several industry lifecycles.

Today's mature industries include food and hospitality, energy, construction, automotive, and financial services.

To a certain extent, an organization's future growth prospects depend on its industry life cycle capabilities and those economic forces driving maturity in their industry. The manufacturing industry is one of the world's most mature industries, having dramatically evolved over the past two centuries. In comparison, the technology industry is relatively young and immature. It is at a stage where acceleration will create a surge of newer innovations at a more rapid pace with gradually longer lifecycles. To understand how the industry can move forward, we will start by inspecting evolving patterns and practices in manufacturing. Some of these early patterns parallel those of the technology industry. We can then look at what is needed to accelerate the tech industry on its journey to maturity and future advancement.

The 1st Revolution	The 2nd Revolution	The 3rd Revolution	The 4th Revolution
-Transition from hand methods to new manufacturing processes. -Introduction of machines, water and steam, factories. -Increased demand and falling prices. -Significant rise in population and incomes.	-Large -scale manufacturing and mass production. -Electricity and steel production.	-Nuclear energy. -Electronics and telecomms. -Computers and the internet. -Space expeditions. -Robots -Biotechnology.	-Connected world. -Enormous processing power and storage capacity. -Access to data and artificial intelligence. -Robotics, autonomous vehicles, 3D printing. -Internet of Things. -Biotechnology -Nanotechnology, energy storage and quantum computing.
c. 1750 - 1840	1870 - 1914	1950 – 2009	2010 – Present day

This chapter aims to explore the characteristics of manufacturing throughout its historical evolution and lifecycles.

The First Industrial Revolution has truly shaped the modern world as we know it. Before the eighteenth century, items, such as textiles, mainly were manufactured on a limited scale by hand, with goods commonly produced on factory lines that could take days, even months, to produce. Production took place largely in a domestic setting where individual workers in primarily rural areas carried out their work within their homes or local premises with highly specialized and labor-intensive processes. Any increase in productivity or output was limited by the geographically scattered, small-scale, and labor-intensive nature of premodern manufacturing. The transport of raw materials, also, was expensive and inefficient, especially where road conditions were difficult, making travel time-consuming.

With the arrival of the steam engine, machines powered by steam appeared from agriculture to textile manufacturing. New innovations emerged with machine tools, and transportation was revolutionized, giving way to urbanization. Factories emerged as workers migrated from farms and villages to cities. Demand for cheaper, mass-produced goods enabled manufacturers to export their items worldwide.

From the late-nineteenth century came a phase of industrial standardization known as the Technological Revolution or, as we know it, the Second Industrial Revolution. We can take a look at how car manufacturing changed during this time and through the ages.

Prior to the 1900s, cars were specially built by craft producers who would typically take several months to make, meaning that more often, fewer than one thousand vehicles were produced each year, which resulted in car ownership being limited to wealthy early adopters. Workmanship depended largely on the skills of the workshop tradesman, and the process was expensive, leading to unpredictable quality and improvement methods. Different manufacturers used their own measurements and tools to craft a vehicle, and so there was a lack of industry-wide standardization of sizes, parts, and production methods. This meant that only a few parts were interchangeable during the build process, making it expensive to manufacture and maintain.

In June 1903, Henry Ford founded the Ford Motor Company. He intended to produce a reasonably priced, efficient, and reliable vehicle available to the masses. Ford wanted to simplify car design to achieve the lowest costs possible. He was the first to integrate an entire production process by pursuing methods that eliminated waste and improved efficiency. Henry Ford realized that he could save significant costs by standardizing parts of the vehicle assembly by reducing the expensive production effort and simplifying the assembly process. He also created the assembly line system with moving platforms and a conveyor system. Cycle times which had previously taken hours dropped to a few minutes. His method increased production efficiency enough for prices to become affordable to the common middle-class consumer.

In this fashion, Ford was able to produce a superior product at lower prices and doubled the minimum daily wage of his assembly workers. The company was at this time making two million Model Ts a year and a significant profit.

The days of mass production

In addition to the increases in manufacturing efficiency, mass production and standardized parts also allowed owners to more easily maintain their vehicles without the heavy reliance on the earlier specialized craft manufacturer and their skilled workers.

By far, mass production improved productivity and greatly increased total production while driving down the net cost of production. This, in turn, made goods more affordable and widely available, which contributed to economic growth.

In the mass-production factory setting, the labor dynamic also changed. There was a significant impact on traditional businesses, jobs, and family life. Factories replaced decentralized shop units, and new industrial conglomerates emerged, gathering large groups of workers in one place. The fabric of the traditional family where the father was in charge of the family and work was largely carried out within the home setting was transformed. Women left home and went to work in factories, domestic service, and coal mines. This provided them with mobility, independent salaries, additional skills, and better living standards.

The process of mass production is demanding and complex, requiring numerous structures, roles, facilities, and disciplines. Companies such as Ford attempted to address this problem by creating specializations and divisions of labor to manage the many different production elements. Industrial engineers, production engineers, repairers, and other specialists managed aspects of the manufacturing process. The main objective was to keep the assembly line moving at all costs because stopping it would mean that factories would fail to meet production targets. The role of assembly workers was diminished to performing one or two simple, specific tasks along the assembly line. They needed minimal training and were seen as low-skilled and easily replaceable. Turnover was high in these factories, and the workers had little or no career progression or specialist training. They had no input in the assembly process other than the performing of their individual tasks.

Workers were to keep near their tools and workspace to eliminate the need to walk away from their assembly line position. Specialist engineers often worked independently of the assembly workers, and some rarely even entered the factory floor despite making important decisions about parts, tooling, tasks, and processes carried out by the assemblers. This arrangement was not without its dysfunctions. The expensive upfront cost of machinery required a high return on investment through their heavy utilization to maintain production targets with the expectation of a low margin for errors.

In manufacturing facilities such as Ford, where the production line had to keep running, defects were identified only at the end of the production line when inspections were carried out in a final inspection phase. Defective vehicles would need significant rework by a separate team whose role was to repair the problems and replace any misaligned parts. This method of identifying faults at the end of production, when an entire batch of products had already been assembled, resulted in wasted effort, materials, and, ultimately, cost. Up to a third of the total effort in the assembly process was invested in the rework area just to fix problems.

The story of Toyota

Toyota Motor Corporation started in 1937. The founder, Kiichiro Toyoda, had earlier traveled to Europe and America to learn more about the car industry, which was in its infancy at that time. Years later, in the 1950s, Eiji Toyoda, a young engineer at Toyota identified opportunities to improve the mass production process.

He noticed there were levels of waste and quality issues which were often only discovered towards the later stage of the manufacturing process. Unlike the organizational silos introduced in mass manufacturing, Toyota sought to increase quality, ownership, responsibility, and collaboration. The result was a skilled workforce empowered and motivated to take ownership of the assembly line. Toyota's workers were trained to identify issues and take responsibility for driving improved quality and efficiency in the factory.

Teams worked around sections of the manufacturing line to assemble parts, perform quality checks, and resolve errors at the source. If they encountered issues they couldn't fix, they would stop the line and fix the problems together before resuming the process. The teams, together with industrial engineers, continually worked together to identify process improvements. They also held quality sessions and conducted root-cause analyses of quality defects. Workers were encouraged to collaborate more effectively. Overall, these changes largely improved the quality of the products and prevented the wasteful rework effort at the post-production stage.

How mass production created waste

Waste can be classified as anything that does not add value to a product or service. It comes in various forms and includes the overproduction of customer orders, over-processing of goods, keeping items in inventory, defects, unused potential of staff members, delays due to waiting periods, and the unnecessary movement and transportation of goods and materials. Indirect waste includes efforts not directly associated with production, such as administrative activities, office politics, and poor efficiency. By calculating these indirect costs, some organizations have found their waste significantly higher than previously thought.

Over-processing refers to inputs spent on features rarely used or that add little or no value to a customer. Defects require extra labor and rework, which are costly in terms of resources, time, and potential customer loss. Moreover, a defective product implies waste at other stages of production, indicating that the system is inefficient. During the production process, a slowing down or halt at any step introduces waiting, which results in reduced productivity and delays in the workflow. This raises the need to improve the efficiency of the process and will require other team members to pile in to speed up the process or improve coordination to make up for the wasted time.

Although it's practically impossible to eliminate all waste, adopting a culture of continuous improvement to reduce waste can draw attention to processes that will help significantly reduce operational costs. Today, a business with an environment based on trust and transparency will encourage its people to proactively identify problems to quickly act to resolve them.

Likewise, organizations today will learn from past lessons that once a product is released, a defect found at this point is significantly more expensive than fixing it at the source. The costs of a customer identifying the defect lead to reduced satisfaction with the product, the risk of customer attrition, and the cost of extra processes within the organization to allocate resources to support and fix the defect.

An evolved team mindset is central to the drive for improved quality where the team takes ownership of eliminating every defect throughout the entire process. For any type of business, the perception of quality is, to an extent, derived from the expectations of their customers, meaning that for them to continue to ensure the satisfaction of their users, they will be required to adopt that meaning into their own processes. Appointing a customer advocate in the organization who acts as the customer's voice will help represent this critical, external perspective to internal staff and, in turn, ensure the meeting of customers' requirements. When identifying defects, the team will fix the problems and the process that led to the defect in the first place, and in so doing, eliminate the potential of its recurrence.

As the car manufacturing industry navigated to maturity, many lessons were learned that can be applied to other modern-day industries. In the late 1970s and early 1980s, Japan's ability to produce high-quality goods at a competitive cost put them ahead of the rest of the world. As a result, companies actively began to invest in quality control techniques. Over the years, industry leaders developed and adopted new methods in their quest for ever-greater efficiency and higher output quality. One of the more popular resulting methods is Lean.

Lean

Lean was born out of the Toyota manufacturing philosophy, which aimed to maximize production efficiency by eliminating waste and other processes that did not add value to the end product. The lean, or just-in-time, production process is refined and organized to produce only what is required for the next stages in the sequence. Throughout the system, just enough is made, stocked, and sequenced as needed with the objective to reduce waste and maintain an even flow. It allows faults and issues to be quickly identified and corrected and, in doing so, to improve productivity, efficiency, cycle time, and costs.

Lean manufacturing has a set of essential principles centered on the value provided to customers. It encourages the practice of continuous improvement and emphasizes the fundamental respect of people. Although Lean was born out of manufacturing, it has been widely adopted by other industries.

The five Lean principles for improving efficiency include defining value, mapping the value stream, creating flow, applying a pull system, and pursuing perfection. The aim is to enable businesses to understand their customers' value and how their products and services can meet those values. In doing so, they can focus on designing products that meet those specific needs and eliminate wasteful effort in producing unwanted features. A value stream is the complete lifecycle of a product, including its design, customer use, and final disposal. Value stream mapping allows businesses to identify and minimize steps that do not add value easily. The flow principle of Lean requires an efficient and steady movement of items from production to shipping without interruption. Equally, the pull-based approach is based on a demand-driven system that creates supply just-in-time to reduce the cost of large inventories and significant amounts of work in progress. Lean requires organizations to seek perfection by creating a culture of continuous improvement.

By applying these principles over time, a lean organization will experience increased efficiency with lower costs, greater productivity, and better quality products that provide value to their customers.

Kanban is a tool used in Lean, developed as a visual method of transparently displaying information between processes through a Kanban board. The method originated when Toyota was looking at ways to improve communication by creating visibility of the manufacturing process. It shows the progression of goods from the automatic scheduling of stock levels to the output of production volumes. Teams can see what work needs to be done and at what stage, allowing them to more quickly identify and fix issues to maintain a steady flow of work. Kanban aims to achieve Just-in-Time production. Toyota's six rules for Kanban are to never pass on defective goods, take only what is needed, produce the exact quantity required, level the production, fine-tune production, and stabilize the process.

Total Quality Management (TQM)

TQM is another qualitative organization-wide management strategy that continuously improves business processes and product quality to enhance customer satisfaction. Its philosophy is to create a permanent environment where all employees are engaged in continuous improvement to provide products and services that increase customer satisfaction. The 'Total' refers to all the departments within an organization, such as sales, marketing, finance, engineering, and design, committed to improving their operations. Although it has its beginnings from the 1920s, it wasn't until 1985 that this approach was recognized and branded "Total Quality Management."

TQM has two key objectives: 100% customer satisfaction and zero defects. Its principles include a strong customer focus with senior management commitment across the organization aiming to achieve many factors, including improvement in cost of quality and customer satisfaction, elimination of waste, zero defects, continuous improvement, and employee empowerment. However, it has its setbacks in that it requires a long-term commitment, which comes at a cost to achieve results. TQM requires commitment right across the company, with all levels of management invested in the program. Without this effort and buy-in, it is unlikely to be a success.

Six Sigma

Similar to Lean, the principles of Six Sigma focus on customer and value, waste and defect reduction, and team collaboration. Initially introduced for manufacturing in 1986 by an American engineer called Bill Smith, who was working for Motorola, Six Sigma is a set of methods and tools to improve business processes and quality management. By improving efficiency and reducing defects, the quality and predictability of product delivery improve — and with it the organization's costs. Six Sigma applies statistical methods to model processes. Business processes can define, measure, analyze, improve, and control defined characteristics in detail through continuous evaluation. A sigma rating describes the maturity of a production process, which indicates its yield or the percentage of defect-free products it creates.

ISO 9001

ISO 9001 is an international standard for a Quality Management System (QMS) set out for an organization to improve the quality of its products and services. It aims to enable businesses to meet their customers' expectations and win their loyalty consistently. Organizations are audited and issued ISO 9001 compliance certification. This standard has key similarities with the other industry models of Lean, TQM, and Six Sigma in many ways. In addition, they can be integrated to form a QMS with the tools and operations to reinforce an organization's specific needs.

The key principles of the ISO QMS are:

- People engagement
- Customer focus
- System approach to leadership
- Process approach
- Continuous improvement
- Factual approach to decision making
- Mutually beneficial supplier relationship

Many of these standard methodologies came out of the research and practices discovered during the early days of mass manufacturing. They continued to be revised as the industry matured to become the practices familiar to many modern industries today.

The purpose of maturity models

Maturity models help businesses assess their overall ability to achieve greater performance against well-defined industrial principles. They are developed as a set of structured stages of capability from a basic foundational layer to more advanced competencies. Well-known models also serve as industry benchmarks so that their market as a whole can make comparisons between organizations in that space. An example of where maturity models can be useful is how an organization is undergoing transformation and requires a supplier to provide services and software. They typically choose to put the project out to tender by issuing an RFP (Request for Proposal) to various suppliers to kick-start a bidding process.

Part of this process might include a lengthy set of questions related to the capabilities required for their solution to assess how well the suppliers will address their needs. The responses will also serve as a means for them to compare each supplier against the others. Some RFP questions can require answers to hundreds of questions, often consuming time and effort across the supplies' businesses. The use of maturity models can provide credibility for a particular business as proof that they have attained the capabilities required to deliver a product or service. In some cases, organizations are only prepared to carry out business with certified suppliers with a particular standard or capability.

There are variants of Lean and Six Sigma maturity models as well as more industry-specific ones. For example, Gartner's five-stage maturity model for manufacturing excellence defines manufacturers' distinct stages of maturity based on their goals, processes, organizational structure, performance management capabilities, and technology. As some organizations mature, improvements in production can move from internal, isolated processes to have a wider impact across their entire supply chain. Some well-known maturity models in information technology include the Capability Maturity Model (CMM or CMMI), which focuses on process improvements, and ITIL maturity aimed at service management. Today there are numerous maturity models which serve core competencies across different areas of industry.

Disruption through innovation

Technology has fundamentally transformed our way of life from how we communicate to how we work, shop, and travel. In the next section, we will look at how instances of technological change have revolutionized the world.

The automotive industry has been proactive in accelerating change in both technological and social areas. To survive, the industry has had to stay current with new innovations and is continuing to advance smart solutions. Car manufacturers have heavily invested in the acquisition of innovative and startup organizations. Features such as in-car integrations with smartphones and dashcams, proximity sensors, and self-driving capabilities have been introduced into vehicles.

Manufacturers continue to optimize their manufacturing processes and the supply chain, which often involves sourcing and storing up to tens of thousands of different components from different locations needed for assembly, just in time to meet shifting consumer demand to maintain cost-effectiveness.

Customer safety and comfort are key to enhancing the consumer's experience as the industry moves towards electric and autonomous vehicles. The car industry pioneered digital automation, with full optimization and robotic automation in use from the shop floor and through the supply chain. Robotic process automation has helped reduce time spent on manual repetitive tasks thereby increasing productivity, and reducing errors and disruptions. Data is collected, visualized, manipulated, analyzed, and acted upon. This has guaranteed better operational reliability and efficiency of manufacturing processes through controls, visualization, and monitoring. Despite its advanced practices, the automotive industry is innovating at an incredible rate. In doing so, firms have created new markets with independent product lifecycles.

The world's top 20 car manufacturers spent £71.7 billion on research and development (R&D) in 2019-20 as the rollout of electric vehicle (EV) ranges gathers pace, according to new research by accountancy and business advisory firm BDO LLP.[1]

BDO's research shows the top 20 manufacturers have collectively invested £341 billion in R&D over the past five years as they race to develop electric vehicles and meet carbon targets.

The amount spent on R&D in the past year is the second-highest on record—lower only to the previous year's £71.9bn total.

Off-the-shelf components for electric vehicles have also become more readily available. This means manufacturers are increasingly purchasing technology from suppliers rather than investing in developing them in-house.

Tesla increased its R&D spend once again last year, investing £1.1 billion, a 10% increase on the previous year. This means that Tesla has now more than doubled its R&D expenditure in the last five years. However, its current spend is less than 10% of the biggest-spending carmaker,

---

[1] Accountancy and business advisory firm BDO LLP provides integrated advice and solutions to help businesses navigate a changing world. Reprinted article Top 20 carmakers' R&D spend tops £70bn in a year Top 20 global carmakers spend another £71.7bn on R&D as electric vehicle rollout gathers pace (published 2021) permission by BDO.

which invested £12.4bn in R&D last year. Within Europe, French and Italian carmakers continued to increase their R&D spending.[2]

[2] Accountancy and business advisory firm BDO LLP provides integrated advice and solutions to help businesses navigate a changing world. Reprinted article Top 20 carmakers' R&D spend tops £70bn in a year (published 2019) permission by BDO.

CHAPTER 2

Lessons Learned Over the Years

We have taken a look at the evolution of a huge and well-established modern industry and its transformation on its journey through maturity towards further accelerated growth. Newer industries can learn similar lessons from the manufacturing industry. Better still, they can apply these insights to accelerate their own growth and, in doing so, become more rapidly established and competitive.

With manufacturing being one of our most mature industries, it has been important to understand the industry's history and look at the key patterns, characteristics, and practices that have emerged in our modern industrial world and influence business today.

A key element that has emerged is the importance of people and the relationships required to sustain the entire supply chain. It might be that products are the output, but at the heart of every step of this process, we find people: people who will benefit from the products, people who will create the products, and people who will supply items to enable the creation of goods.

Getting to know your customer and the value your business provides is essential. It requires that you engage with your customers to the point where you truly understand their habits and needs, which establishes their long-term loyalty. Knowing your customer and representing them through your production process will ensure that their requirements are satisfied and, most importantly, that they trust you.

There are various ways organizations can learn more about their customer, which might be facilitated through the role of a customer advocate who can act as a representative of the customer's voice within an organization. Gathering information from the customer through their use of the product and periodically asking them for their feedback will increase their users' knowledge and allow them to offer the right amount of choice and variety. The entire organization needs to be engaged in objectives and measures to deliver value and improve customer satisfaction.

As well as building strong customer relationships, it is also important to develop partnerships based on loyalty and mutual trust with suppliers. Toyota went as far as to invest in their suppliers' businesses and treat them as partners. As a result, their suppliers began to understand their products and processes intimately. They were able to respond more readily to changes that could have negatively impacted their own businesses, hence creating a win-win outcome. This type of relationship can, in turn, convert suppliers into advocates of the organization's brand.

Today, it is widely documented that having a workforce empowered and motivated, where teams take ownership of continuously improving their products and practices, will bring the organization closer to achieving its goals. It requires a culture where leaders recognize their people as their most strategic asset and are prepared to give them the autonomy and trust to make the right decisions. To achieve the best possible outcomes for an organization and its people, people will need to grow to maximize their skills and potential. This will then allow them to take on new challenges and so continue to build a sustainable business.

A culture of continuous improvement within an organization is another key factor that emerged from the Second Industrial Revolution. Continuous review and optimization take into account that customer requirements and technologies are constantly changing. Efficiency improvements that seek to eliminate waste, reduce complexity, and improve quality are made more responsive to adapting and staying competitive.

Since organizations like Toyota in the car industry demonstrated the dominant impact quality improvement could have, there has been significant investment in quality improvement practices. Quality has been shown to be one of the key criteria for a business to achieve industry maturity. It allows businesses to increase revenue and achieve a competitive advantage, and it also helps them establish market share through brand loyalty and trust.

The technological advances of the first two industrial revolutions brought about change in the production of goods, the standardization of products and processes, machine automation, and the methods and tools to improve quality and production output. Today's businesses now have a vast range of well-defined standardized practices applicable across multiple industries, not just in manufacturing, without needing to reinvent the wheel.

As one of our oldest and mature industries, manufacturing has continued to re-invent itself. To survive rapid change in technologies, markets, consumer habits, and environmental demands, industry players have recognized the necessity of investing in innovation to keep abreast with technological advancements.

CHAPTER 3

Emergence of the Modern Technology Industry

The Third Industrial Revolution, also known as the Digital Revolution, began in the 1950s with the introduction of digital electronics, the mainframe, followed by personal computing, digital telephony, the Internet, mobile phones, and social media as new forms of communication. These technologies have marked today's Information Age.

Computer hardware and mainframes came into use from the 1940s and became more commonplace in the 1950s. Just as with the beginnings of the First Industrial Revolution, the software industry started with a few specialist 'craft' engineers who had access to the first computers — mostly mainframes. Computers were programmed with machine code instructions using punch cards. Programmers didn't directly interact with the machines but instead delivered cards by hand to technicians who set up batch processes on the computers. The batch processes would typically take hours to complete, and the results would then be sent back to the programmers to analyze. At that time, women largely performed these programming tasks. Fortran and Cobol were the early programming languages to appear during this time, with legends such as Grace Hopper being one of the pioneers of programming languages and operating systems.

The software used on the mainframes during the 1960s was proprietary, with machine instructions specific to hardware. A vast number of high-level software languages were already in existence, and a growing number of organizations produced and sold software. However, software costs were high, and only a few organizations had the resources to fund large, expensive custom software engineering projects. In those early days of programming, projects consistently failed to deliver quality solutions on time and budget, leading the development community to recognize the absence of proper best practices, processes, or standards required to produce software commercially.

The term "software engineering" was introduced in 1968, around the time of the first NATO (North Atlantic Treaty Organization) Software Engineering Conference, during a period when software engineering was seen to be at a point of crisis. The conference's goal was to improve the practice as a discipline as interests grew to define better tools and approaches for designing and implementing complex systems.

With the arrival of the personal computer in the 1970s and 80s came new programming languages and tools. Universities started to offer degrees in computer science and engineering, and more men started to enroll in these courses as they started to express an interest in computers and programming. During this decade, the ratio of women to men started to shift as the industry required college and university degrees to obtain work. With far fewer women entering higher education to study computer science compared to their male counterparts, the population of women in technology declined, leading to the male-dominated characteristics that exist today. The resulting lack of diversity and inclusion is a topic of discussion on its own and will be touched upon later in the book.

The first handheld mobile phones arrived in the 1970s with the development of cellular networks. Over the decades, various generations of cellular telephony have been developed from 1G through 5G. Mobile phones have consumed daily life, with device features evolving from a primary purpose of telephone voice calls to text messaging, photography, and now much more. Today's smartphones have opened up new means of communication, with social media growing in popularity for all types of interactions. Mobile telephony and social networks have transformed the way we live, how we do business, purchase goods and services and even develop relationships, making it possible to communicate with people we've never met almost instantaneously.

Never have people been able to access such a plethora of freely available information. A 2021 publication by Hootsuite & We Are Social, "Digital 2021: Global Overview Report" (https://datareportal.com/reports/digital-2021-global-overview-report) shows that:

Mobile: 5.22 billion people use a mobile phone today, equating to 66.6 percent of the world's total population. Unique mobile users have grown by 1.8 percent (93 million) since January 2020, while the total number of mobile connections has increased by 72 million (0.9 percent) to reach a total of 8.02 billion at the start of 2021.

Internet: 4.66 billion people around the world use the internet in January 2021, up by 316 million (7.3 percent) since this time last year. Global internet penetration now stands at 59.5 percent.

Social media: there are now 4.20 billion social media users around the world. This figure has grown by 490 million over the past 12 months, delivering year-on-year growth of more than 13 percent. The number of social media users is now equivalent to more than 53 percent of the world's total population.

The typical user now spends 2 hours and 25 minutes on social media each day, equating to roughly one full waking day of their life each week.

Since the 1960s, attempts have been made to improve the industry's maturity, not only in terms of software engineering disciplines but also with the processes that drive the creation of software products. Over time, software engineering roles have evolved into sub-disciplines such as requirements engineering, software architecture and design, data engineering, development, quality assurance, and release engineering. Writing software has become a profession concerned with how best to maximize software quality and make it appealing to its users.

The production of software is the set of methods, tools, and processes involved in taking an idea through the stages of design and manufacture, or rather implementation, to arrive at the finished product. The various stages involve design and prototyping, software development, quality assurance, release, and customization. During the development phase, code is written and may be assembled from various standardized components and services. Several approaches to delivering software have been applied with the most popular ones being the Waterfall method, Rapid Application Development (RAD), Agile, and DevOps.

The Waterfall method, introduced in 1970, dominated the development approach for software in the 1980s. However, frustration grew over long time-lags and lack of flexibility with decisions made early in a project. Around the same period, other industries, such as the automobile industry, were undergoing transformation. Whereas it previously took the car industry six years or more to design a new vehicle, by the 1990s that time was cut almost in half.

Certain attempts were made to promote iterative software development. In the 1990s, various methods evolved in reaction to the rigid, heavyweight Waterfall approach. These included RAD, Unified Process, and Dynamic Systems Development Method or DSDM. In the early 1990s, Scrum was created, and later the "Scrum Software Development Process" was published, followed in 2001 by the Agile Manifesto. Agile ideology gained huge popularity among the developer community and adoption has become widespread since its inception. However, there are gaps that don't account for the full delivery cycle across an organization. The Scaled Agile Framework (SaFe) was later introduced to fulfill the need to scale Agile right across the enterprise.

Software engineering and the industry around software are still comparatively immature. One of the core issues in software engineering is that its approaches are rarely empirical. Quality practices, development standards, and approaches to producing software for the end-user vary widely from one organization to the next. The result is that customers have widely different experiences across the suite of software solutions they utilize each day to run their businesses and livelihoods. To improve the status of the industry, well-defined engineering approaches to problem-solving would need to be applied. Frameworks, patterns, tools, and methods that can be widely shared and adopted across the industry to establish consistent levels of quality and more predictable mechanisms for delivering software will provide customers with a more consistent and equitable return on their investment.

There have been calls for licensing, certification, and regulation of software practices as a mechanism for maturing this field. In some countries, such as Canada, a Canadian Information Processing Society has established an Information Systems Professional certification process. Bodies such as the Institute of Electrical and Electronics Engineers, or IEEE, continue to raise standards in the software industry and have defined standards for software and systems engineering aspects. Ultimately, users of software products will enjoy a more consistent experience when they sit in front of a piece of software and start to use it.

The modern world's fourth industrial revolution, also labeled as Industry 4.0, where the digital and real world interconnect, builds on the foundations that were laid by the third industrial revolution, the digital revolution. With computing and the internet brought greater access to people and information, and with significantly increased compute power and storage, came the provision of more data which has become widely accessible. In addition, electronics, sensors, analytics, machine learning, and artificial intelligence are driving automation, robotics, and innovations such as autonomous vehicles. Following these advancements is the drive towards the democratization of manufacturing through the likes of 3-D printing.

CHAPTER 4

Building a Product

Start with the idea

The creation or enhancement of any technology or product starts from an idea or concept. The need for a change could result from a new market opportunity, an innovation, a requirement from a customer, or a strategic business driver.

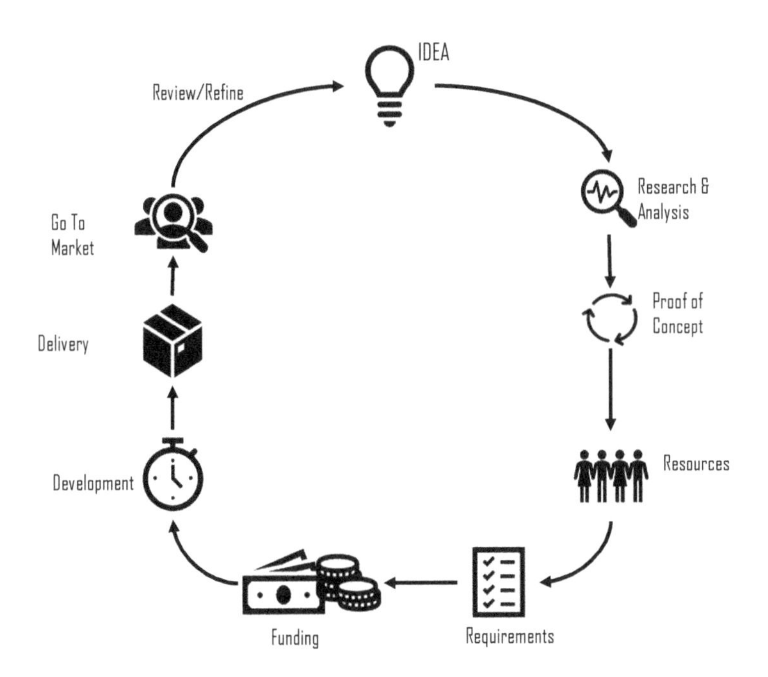

The process to take a product from ideation to production is best approached through a well-defined framework starting with a clear definition of goals and scope. Furthermore, the need for sufficient time, budget, and alignment with customers and stakeholders will provide a firm footing for the successful launch and lifetime of that product. The lean start-up or lean inception approach for the early stage of a product or major feature favors discovery and test of the idea with customer feedback in place of an initial heavyweight design to learn what customers want and define a minimal viable product. This faster and more accurate method is preferable to the guessing exercise and big upfront planning often applied to products.

The initial step should always be to consider how an idea aligns with the organization's strategy. What benefits will a product provide? What growth opportunities will it present, and ultimately what value will it bring customers. Research at this stage requires an understanding of markets, trends, competition, and any legal concerns. Work at this stage should take place across teams. If the research stacks up, the next stage is to test out the concept.

Prove the concept

If the idea shows promise, a more detailed understanding of whether the customer will adopt a product or service is necessary. In addition, will the business have the means to bring the idea to market? Will the idea be financially and technically viable?

A Proof of Concept (PoC), or experiment, tests this feasibility by allowing the business to verify that the concept is fit for purpose. It is useful where, for instance, an idea might be a fundamental game-changer, unquantified complexity, untested approach, innovation, or new technology or tool. In each of these cases, an assessment is needed to help determine whether the idea could achieve its necessary objectives. It's worth noting that not every idea needs a PoC, such as in the case where an existing feature requires a well-understood and desired enhancement.

A small cross-functional team with representatives from across the business should run the PoC. Together, the product manager, strategy team, and project sponsor should define a minimal set of requirements and success criteria for the PoC to test the initial questions and unknowns. The success criteria are important in deciding whether the business should move ahead with the product idea.

Examples of the types of questions that might require confirmation are whether the product is technically feasible, marketable, supported with the current resources, fits within cost expectations, minimizes complexity, can be maintained and supported, or can be seamlessly configured. Finally, does the organization have the skills and resources needed to take the product to market?

At this stage, it's tempting for a business to bring a technical team alone into developing a prototype and then to provide details of development estimate and cost. However, this could be a misstep leading to a narrow view and potentially fraught with undiscovered risks. There are so many more factors that determine a successful PoC, and to test out the concept requires inputs from across the business. Each person involved in the PoC must know exactly what their role is and what is expected of them for the outcome of the exercise. Such a cross-functional team should be fully dedicated to the task and released from other activities within their departments for the period of the PoC. A short, time-boxed duration is usually more acceptable within the business and more likely to achieve a successful outcome.

The scope of the PoC must be well-defined and focused on questions that require answers to specific questions to arrive more rapidly to a conclusion that determines whether or not it achieves its ultimate aims. The team should actively identify, capture, and review risks and dependencies during this period and ideally record them on a visible and easily accessible tool for the business to review.

Test it

Now that a prototype exists, this is the time to engage with a large enough sample of the user base that can provide sufficient feedback. This is a relatively inexpensive and essential exercise to gauge the response of the market to the idea.

There are different methods to conduct trials. For example, you might choose to bring users together for a guided session or work with a few at a time to record and monitor their interactions with the product. Whichever you prefer, by the end of the trial, you should have a good set of data that supports an understanding of whether your market endorses the idea and prototype, will be valuable, and essentially adopted by its users. The data will also present the scope for defining minimal product features.

Address the risks

During the PoC, log risks and challenges. Address issues through user feedback. Together, these are captured and assessed by the team.

Each item is ranked and evaluated to determine how best any issues can be mitigated, if necessary. Where different approaches for the same solution are captured, the team will define the levels of complexity, approximate execution effort or time, cost to implement, resource requirements, etc. Together, these will provide a clearer definition of the solution to take in building the product.

Decision time: Go / No-Go

At the end of the activity, all participants of the PoC, along with the product sponsor and other key decision-makers, review the outcomes and assess them alongside the success criteria. A formal decision will be made to decide whether to proceed with the next stage - the product creation.

It is important at this stage that decisions and actions are agreed regarding the risks and options defined earlier in the process. These should, in time, be shared with the teams that will develop the product and the product manager to ensure that they are proactively addressed.

If the decision is to proceed, set aside a budget to fund the delivery program. The team that drove the PoC might at this stage be disbanded and returned to their departments or projects. In the ideal situation, these people with the initial product knowledge will work within their teams to kick off the product development. The PoC activity is closed and the initial development environment archived as the team moves into the production phase.

Route-to-Market: Create the roadmap

This is the first formal step towards creating the product - the definition of a fully functioning solution that will make its way to market. Data from the earlier stages of ideation is used in the roadmap definition process, along with other information based on trends, competitor products, market data, and customer and stakeholder feedback.

The Minimal Viable Product (MVP) is a useful tool for gaining critical feedback from early adopters by defining the most valuable features that would be sufficient to reach the core user group. This early feedback will support the approach of continuous improvement and adaptation as the product continues through iterations.

As well as traditional methods of receiving customer feedback through interviews and surveys, user-generated data directly within the product itself can provide rapid and very helpful insights. This type of data can be more accurate for gaining a real-time understanding of the user, their habits, and those features of the product that appear to be of most value. The information will help the organization identify product investment areas to help improve customer satisfaction and prevent over-processing of product features. User data can also proactively show details of faults and issues, such as performance bottlenecks that can be resolved, sometimes without the customer even knowing that they exist. Having this data will also reduce the time and effort required to troubleshoot and fix problems.

Regular user forums are another method of soliciting feedback from customers. These forums are mostly held face-to-face and bring customers together to discuss their shared experiences. In my own experience of running or participating in such sessions, we can gain valuable insights from listening to customers discussing their experiences, the issues they faced, and ultimately what benefits they acquired. I also found that they would act as a support group to each other in responding to questions and sharing their own experiences of how they could resolve specific problems. Our customers were passionate and enthusiastic about our products. They felt valued and were keen to contribute to discussions, share feedback, and suggest further improvements to the product, which would help solve their business problems.

Visiting customers and having one-to-one time with them as a means to continue to develop a working relationship is highly recommended and, as I found, well received. Along with this is the ability to access data from internal customer support systems to understand specific user requirements and the challenges they may have faced. All of this data and the strategic business goals provide valuable inputs for the product roadmap.

A few years ago, I helped a project having difficulty with developing a new feature. Towards the feature release date, questions started to surface across the business on the feature's objectives, key functions, installation, and configuration. The training team had no understanding of the solution and was stuck on preparing training programs for customers and business partners. The customer support team felt they did not have sufficient technical knowledge. Marketing had started to ask their own questions about the feature's functionality, which they needed to prepare their marketing activities. The release engineering team was scratching their heads on deploying in a cloud environment as it partly relied on some non-cloud components. In a nutshell, the release was becoming a nightmare.

The strategic goal for this feature had been clear from the outset, so what had happened? The PoC was rushed and ill-defined. A handful of engineers had been assembled to develop the required functionality and integrate third-party components into the product to demonstrate that the integration was successful. However, beyond that, the requirements to determine its feasibility for the market and with stakeholders hadn't been clearly defined. As a result, there was no clarity over what a successful outcome looked like. Furthermore, there was little involvement with other parts of the business. The prototype hadn't been reviewed by potential users either internally or externally, so no feedback confirmed the solution's viability.

Once the decision was made to proceed with product development, the developers continued to work in the PoC environment, isolated from the main production infrastructure. When the code was ready, merging it into the main environment led to inconsistencies and errors, causing delays to the project when additional rework was necessary.

The key lessons from this were that a clear objective is necessary to identify a successful outcome of a PoC. Engagement across the organization must be part of the process. When concluding the exercise, decide whether it makes business sense to proceed with an idea based on predetermined criteria. Making the decision triggers the production process with work being carried out in the right environment to support the delivery of high-quality software.

A software product has a lifecycle that evolves through various stages, from initial idea and innovation through its journey into maturity and eventual demise. After the product has proven the initial concept, it starts the innovation stage. Next, early adopters come on board, willing to accept the risk of testing the new product to see its potential and serve the purpose of providing feedback within their communities and the wider market. Finally, as the product enters its growth phase, with the minimum viable product (or MVP) being generally available to the market, early adopters will start to come on board to purchase the product, usually at a time when the price is at a premium.

The MVP tests the market to determine what is valuable, usable, and feasible for a small group of the most relevant users. If this proves the product's objectives, the product can be developed incrementally over time. As the majority of lifecycle customers adopt the product, it stabilizes and typically becomes more affordable. The product moves into maturity with regular refinements and evolutions until eventually, it reaches end-of-life.

A product might go through several rounds of innovation during its lifetime, introducing new capabilities and potentially opening up new market opportunities. Existing users can become the early adopters of those features before their eventual general availability. In some cases, the innovation might not make its way into the product if early feedback contradicts the desired outcome. While investment in further innovation is relatively low at this early stage, user engagement can help the business determine whether to proceed.

Take the example of Google Glass, an optical head-mounted pair of glasses that captured and displayed information in a hands-free format, originally launched in 2013. The prototype was sold to early, qualified "Glass Explorers" at the premium price of $1,500. However, after two years and poor reviews, Google discontinued development. Some criticism cited a failure to deliver innovation with a clear purpose or function, concerns over privacy matters, technical issues, and unattractiveness. Uncertain of the problem it was solving, there was little direction to develop the prototype, and soon its early adopters turned to social media to share their negative experiences. Google has, however, since been able to launch a new, improved Glass.

The evolution of a product requires the iterative gathering and analysis of business intelligence from various sources based on market feedback, customer interviews, and early user testing. In addition, data is obtained from stakeholders within the business as part of competitor assessments, trend analysis, and technology surveys. All of this data will be prioritized and laid out to define the vision and strategy of the product. There will often be many competing priorities, and efficiency requires a product manager (PM) highly skilled at communicating and collaborating with a broad range of stakeholders. They will need to be transparent throughout the roadmap process and assertive in communicating the justifications behind decisions to bring everyone on board. Here, the term product manager, or PM, represents this role in defining the product's direction.

Businesses that operate in silos will play out a product management scene: the product manager focuses purely on roadmap definition with customers, business strategy, and commercial functions. Decisions are made at the top, including estimates on when features will be released, and these are used to define the roadmap. At this point, after the commitment has been communicated to the ecosystem, the development teams are asked to deliver the solution.

This kind of cold start approach is likely to be beset with numerous problems, most likely low team engagement, wasted time explaining the product vision, answers to countless questions, and needing to untangle undiscovered issues which could hinder progress. These types of projects tend to run into difficulties and most likely overrun, adding unnecessary pressure to the teams and resulting in frustrations from customers and stakeholders.

The key lesson here is to bring the development teams into the process early and ensure widespread alignment and consensus on the roadmap. The stronger the alignment across a business, particularly regarding communication of strategic goals, the higher chance the business will achieve its ambitions. A lack of harmonization across a relatively immature business suggests that the business is operating in an ad hoc and potentially reactive state lacking in focus of their objectives, whilst a more advanced business will exhibit characteristics where the entire business is more focused on achieving goals with established processes and activities to drive alignment.

Taking this further, organizations that have completed several iterations of learnings and improvements, will have matured their alignment across the business by integrating key functions with business planning activities and connected processes to promote greater collaboration and communication in a way that is likely to achieve successful outcomes consistently.

Focus on delivering value

"Our highest priority is to satisfy customers through early and continuous delivery of valuable software." [3]

One of the key aims of the product management role is to maximize products and services that deliver valuable benefits to their customers, sufficient to drive strong user adoption, grow the business, and potentially disrupt the market in line with the organization's long-term vision and strategy.

What is value?

Value is often associated with financial indicators, such as how much an organization makes and its growth or retention of market share. The Harvard Business Review article, "What Customers Value," defines value in business markets as "the worth in monetary terms of the technical, economic, service and social benefits a customer

---

[3] The Agile Manifesto agilealliance.org. the Agile Manifesto authors: Kent Beck Mike Beedle Arie van Bennekum Alistair Cockburn Ward Cunningham Martin Fowler Robert C. Martin Steve Mellor Dave Thomas James Grenning Jim Highsmith Andrew Hunt Ron Jeffries Jon Kern Brian Marick Ken Schwaber Jeff Sutherland © 2001.

organization receives in exchange for the price it pays for a market offering."[4]

Not all value is financially motivated. Some benefits may apply to a business or its customers that are intangible and difficult to measure in financial terms. This type of value could be in terms of customer satisfaction related to the customer's experience of products or services offered to them. Value can also refer to an organization's brand identity and reputation and its assets, including intellectual property, people and culture, or domain expertise. However defined, it is vital to determine how a product or service can deliver value to customers and prospects.

A product manager's key role is to share the vision, strategic objectives, and value proposition of the product and its features with the business and the teams taking it to market. This global alignment will ensure that everyone understands the goals and how they can achieve them. It also helps reduce functional boundaries within organizations by enabling people to speak in common terms and work with a common mindset towards the same

---

[4] Reprinted by permission of Harvard Business Review. (Excerpt/Exhibit) from *Understand What Customers Value* by James C. Andersen and James A. Narus, issue November-December 1998.

goals and success criteria. When discussing product roadmap requirements, this acts as a facilitation tool in ensuring that the conversations maintain a united, outcomes-based focus on the value themes. Each major piece of work should include a value tag, meaning the expected financial, customer, strategic, and product benefits.

Cost, value, price

Businesses can become fixated with story points, productivity, and velocity as a means of understanding the realization of value from product deliveries. However, this is only part of the whole picture. What matters is how soon we create business value. In other words, are the requirements and priorities well defined and understood? It's easy to see why those metrics of velocity and productivity become more important: they are quantifiable yet easy to misinterpret. These measures in isolation often don't mean much overall if the employees focus on quickly building the wrong product or delivering lower value to the market.

In situations where entire teams are following the path of developing software without understanding the value likely to be derived, those products and projects are likely to fail. This is because that upfront effort to share the vision, objectives, purpose, and anticipated measurable outcomes are often missed, or priorities are not strictly defined and followed. Engineers are generally intelligent professionals who can design solutions that can successfully achieve those business needs when they understand a requirement. It helps them focus on the value that needs to be realized—it helps them know WHY.

Building a product and releasing it to market is an investment. A team has a budget, say $1000, which will be invested in a product to produce a return of three times the amount invested. In turn, you can invest the profits on future projects. At each point, you aim to produce sufficient value to invest in the next project. Thinking about it this way helps you drive a value-led approach to product development, particularly how you define the priorities to achieve greater outcomes sooner.

The moment the product is released is the time to start measuring value based on predefined metrics. For instance, if you wanted to gather insights into user adoption, one way would be to build analytics into your product to collect usage data regularly. Customer feedback, satisfaction metrics, and Net Promoter Scores (NPS) are all complementary metrics that measure intangible benefits and drive loyalty and retention. Releasing valuable software early and frequently provides faster feedback loops, which will provide early visibility into the realization of value to the market. Key Value Indicators (KVIs) are metrics that identify how a product or solution is impactful and adding value. They do not directly tie into financial benefits. Instead, assess metrics based on both their positive and negative impacts to implement performance improvements. KVIs are defined based on what your organization defines as value. For example, if your product is business-critical to your customers, you would consider defining KVIs around system availability and performance.

Work with themes

Define roadmaps by a set of features with planned delivery over time. I rarely see a roadmap that talks about problems that a product seeks to fulfill or the value that needs to be realized. Instead, the product roadmap is a tool to communicate the strategic direction of the product. It tells a story about the value it delivers, the pain points it addresses, and the metrics that measure its success.

Themes represent the high-level product problems that need solving. A theme might go something like: "Hey, our customers are spending hours having to export data from one system into spreadsheets, wrangling the data, and then importing it into our systems. How can we improve their experience so that they can automatically merge their data into our system in the right format and save time and effort?" This is quite different from features defining specific functional requirements. For instance, a feature to solve this customer problem would be integrating external data directly from an external customer system into our system. Understanding the situation described in a theme provides context. It enables development teams to empathize with their customers' problems and focus on resolving those problems. Marketing can create content around the story and sales teams, and armed with a better understanding will connect more successfully with prospects.

Themes can also be useful as a tool to track progress across multiple teams involved in taking a product to market. Presenting a roadmap using themes helps to more easily convey the messaging and justification of the product's strategy to diverse stakeholders. This also provides the vision and the 'why' to the teams that will ultimately deliver the solution. Each theme should contain a high-level strategic objective, a description of what it aims to achieve or what problem it seeks to solve, and a set of measurable metrics to determine how it might meet expectations in market terms. The metrics might include elements such as customer satisfaction, revenue, or user adoption.

Theme

Name
Strategic Objective
Category
Value
Statement of benefits
Acceptance Criteria
Description

The theme's category explains the desired improvement. For instance, are we aiming to attract new market opportunities, offer competitive differentiation, develop a new innovation, or address a technical debt? In this way, it should be clear to stakeholders what justifications there are for the investment and what outcomes they expect. This will help facilitate discussions to achieve better alignment across the business. Ultimately, the professional teams who build the product will want to know:

- What are we building?
- Why are we doing this?
- Who are we doing it for?
- How does the solution support end-users?

Being presented with the problem allows them to identify the right solution to work towards more efficiently.

In time, the theme iteratively divides into a set of related epics or features, which divides into stories in a product backlog. Development teams collect related stories to deliver a Minimum Marketable Feature (MMF) or an Epic. These can be interchangeable depending on how one chooses to manage them, but ultimately the desire is to have a set of deliverables representing a unit of value.

A MMF is a self-contained unit of deliverable software which has significant value. Knowing the value propositions, the MMF contains stories that development teams work on until the MMF is ready to be released, hence realizing customer value early. As a feature, and unlike a theme, the MMF will describe a piece of valuable functionality that will form part of the solution to address the problem defined in the higher-level theme.

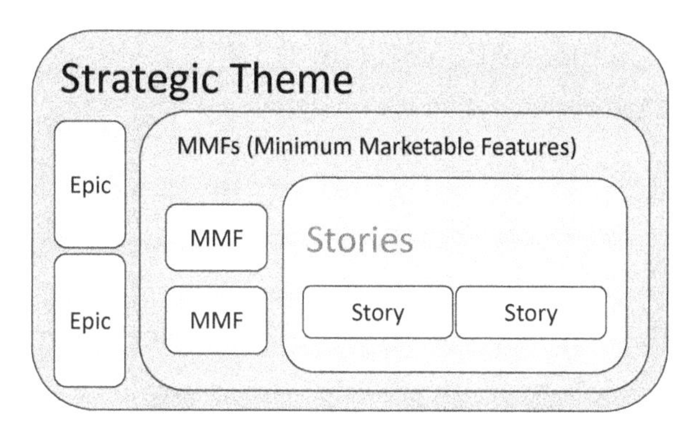

Typically, a MMF contains several stories. Each MMF is estimated in terms of effort and prioritized. When it comes to release planning, the valuable themes, epics, and MMFs are selected to represent the Minimum Viable Product (MVP) deliverables to get early feedback to prove that the concept achieves its aims.

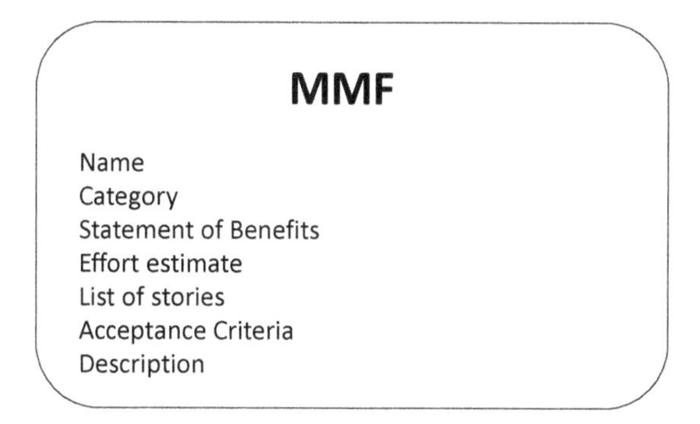

The category can represent any of the following:

- Competitive differentiation
- Revenue generation
- Cost-saving
- Brand projection
- Commercial opportunity
- Customer loyalty/satisfaction

Now, next, later

One of the aims of a roadmap is to show the current, short-term, and longer-term priorities for a product. Business roadmaps that show items delivered on precise dates or even months in the distant future set themselves up for failure. Most industries face rapid and continuous change, so priorities will likely shift. Making firm commitments by dates will seriously impact stakeholders' expectations, leading to disappointment and possible reputation damage. For teams involved in delivering solutions, this places them unfairly under a lot of pressure. The most likely outcome will be poor quality product releases and workforce burnout.

Now, Next, Later is a refreshing approach that shifts the focus from fixed dates to priorities, allowing for a more predictable and flexible method of setting product expectations while managing the evolving business landscape. How does this work?

Near-term work items are *Now*. Items that are ready for release or due in the coming period are represented in the Now bucket. Items that are being worked on and prioritized for the next period sit in Next. Items considered for prioritization further down the line are in the Later bucket. The organization defines timelines for each of the buckets. So, for instance, *Now* might indicate items to prepare for release in the current quarter as development is actively progressing or nearly done. The details are well understood and commitments can be shared with stakeholders. *Next* items go in the Now bucket. Themes and epics can be refined, and teams can define the features and initial stories for prioritization and estimates more clearly. *Later*, then, is a parking place for ideas and high-level business requirements, which will be prioritized for future releases.

In this way, priorities can be more predictably managed. Once near-term work is scheduled and in progress, there is no need to change planning details around these tasks, and their details and expected availability can be reliably shared with the market. For Later items, stakeholders and development teams can influence and contribute to the requirements, definitions, and priorities. The backlog items iteratively move through the priority buckets. In turn, product management and the rest of the business can share development status with customers without needing to commit to dates long in the future.

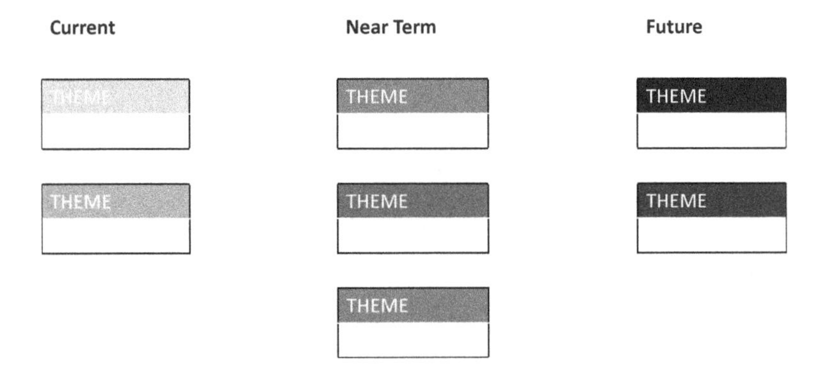

The impact mapping technique

As previously mentioned, themes that explain the problems to be solved and define the value attached to solving the problem are useful in determining a product roadmap or set of priorities. The breakdown of themes into epics and eventually into stories requires a collaborative approach initiated by the product manager with customers, the business, and development teams working together to define requirements and estimate the efforts necessary to deliver valuable software.

Experience has shown that sharing the strategic product goals and expected benefits early and often with teams improves the product's success through alignment. It also helps delivery teams challenge their thinking and avoid deviation from the main goals where there is a temptation to introduce scope creep.

Impact mapping is a powerful way of accelerating preparation and alignment across the business to focus on the desired outcomes during roadmap definition and planning. I first came across this technique several years ago when I attended my first ever Behavioral Driven Development (BDD) conference in London. Some years later, I was involved in the early stages of the roadmap process for my company, where we applied the impact mapping method. We held a full-day workshop involving various teams from across the business who would drive the product to market.

We worked together following introductory exercises and breakout sessions, starting with the strategic goals and vision to define an impact map using cards and post-it notes. We ended up with a set of high-level features prioritized based on specific business criteria. The exercise was worthwhile — focused, dynamic, collaborative, and efficient. Most importantly, within a short period, we had achieved our common goal. We identified potential pitfalls and dependencies which would probably not have been achieved without everyone in the same room. After a more detailed analysis and prioritization, we all returned to revisit the roadmap together. When it came to roadmap project kick-offs, we recognized how well aligned we were with the expectations of the product and the goals it set out to achieve.

During project implementations, we efficiently delivered the solution through a strong spirit of collaboration and understanding. Through the practice of roadmap definition involving participants from across the business, teams were on board with the roadmap, with everyone speaking the same language and working towards common strategic goals.

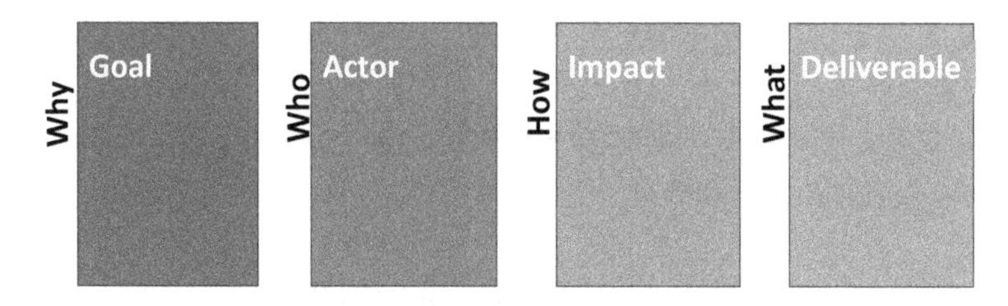

The idea of impact mapping is that we align high-level strategic business goals to the software change required. Create a mind map to identify the impact on peoples' behaviors and determine various solutions to satisfy the goal. Then, define assumptions made while capturing the key problem statements.

Using a mind map approach helps identify actors that are impacted by the change. Capturing their pain points can connect how the expected change is likely to modify their behavior with the understanding of how it will address their challenges. Conducting this exercise allows participants to define a set of deliverables that will potentially add value and improve customer satisfaction. Perform business analysis on the most relevant and valuable items to customers to form the highest priority items that will then make their way onto the product, release, or backlog.

Take, for example, a market where your customers have a problem managing and tracking change requests within their own business. They require an audit trail of changes that have been requested, in progress, and authorized. The individuals who manage their business changes apply inconsistent approaches through various means, including emails, spreadsheets, and informal verbal conversations, making it challenging to trace. Your organization is providing a solution to this market. In consulting with their customers, it has been identified that introducing a change-management feature to their product will create value for customers, leading to competitive advantage and increased product revenue.

During your impact mapping workshop, you will first identify the actors impacted by the feature—in other words, managing change requests. The list of actors includes the change requester who needs a change to be made; the reviewer who observes the status of all change requests in the business; the authorizer who reviews, approves, or rejects a change; and the change agent who performs the change and confirms when it has been actioned. The resulting system will need to manage the status of each change request and notify actors at various stages in the process. In addition, a system administrator is required to manage access permissions and levels of authorization for users of the system.

For each set of actors, you will map out the impacts throughout the change request process. I also recommend that you capture any questions and specific scenarios that will need testing at some stage during the development of the feature, with some of these becoming the acceptance criteria required to meet the feature's goals. Once defining the impacts for each actor has been completed, work is done to define a range of ideas that will become deliverables for the solution, captured and grouped by order of priority.

Plan for release

Now that the product roadmap has been adapted, featuring the most valuable strategic items first, it's time to prepare for their development. Release planning defines the feature creation sequence. If you are applying the Now, Next, Later approach, these features will be placed into your Next bucket to be prepared for the product's subsequent release.

The best way to carry out release planning is to bring together the people involved in delivering the product. In addition to the engineering team, include expert teams such as the customer training department, customer support, implementation consultants, and marketing. Together, they share the vision and objectives for the release and gather all the elements for consideration. This might include requirements from each team, for instance, requirements for supporting training and implementation, tools and utilities to support upgrades, customizations or installation, certain types of test data, and documentation for knowledge transfer. There might also be dependencies to consider or new technologies which would require additional skills, resources, or training. Finally, collectively identify the risks and challenges that might impact the project. Altogether, this provides a comprehensive and more realistic scope of requirements to include in the release backlog.

In the release planning stage, expert teams will work together to estimate feature scope, giving an early indication of how many iterations or timeframes it might take to deliver the solution. It is important to communicate these high-level estimates as an indicator instead of a promise of a timeframe for delivery. High-level items will iteratively be organized and broken down into smaller, more manageable pieces of work, which will feature in the product backlog. The release plan might present these as projects to be implemented by several teams working in parallel across the business.

Based on estimates and historical team performance figures, use a capacity plan to determine the approximate length of time it could take to implement a piece of work. Some contingency will need to be included based on any earlier assumptions. Most importantly, the expert teams must buy into these plans before communicating to the business. Sharing the plan helps to see the bigger picture, understand the effort required, and the risks and assumptions that might influence the project timelines. Ongoing monitoring, tracking, and review of progress are necessary to raise any deviation from the expected timescale as early as possible while presenting options that can pivot the project towards the desired timeframe.

Did it meet the expectations?

By connecting business goals to deliverables, everyone understands the value of the product. Once released to market, if the solution doesn't fully meet the desired outcomes, the business will adapt their initial assumptions, knowing that they better understand their market's needs.

Such a feedback loop is essential for development teams as they proceed further with improving the product. This is often the missing piece in its lifecycle. Once customers are using the product, what was their experience? What did they like, and more importantly, which parts did they find the most valuable? How did it benefit them day-to-day?

What issues took customers the most time and effort to overcome, and how can this be improved? These questions are important in evolving the product, adding value, and gaining customer loyalty. Imagine the customer's excitement and relief when a much-improved feature has eradicated one of their challenges in the next phase! And yet, these details rarely find their way back to the experts building the product. Instead, they find themselves on a turning wheel of more and more packed features, and as they work on these, they are less intimately connected to the impact they are making.

Having invested so much in building the product, the product manager needs to ensure that the measurable outcomes are quickly followed up after the product's release. Insights from the market should be collected and shared across the business.

As the organization learns more about their customers and how they use the product, they will become more effective in tailoring future requirements to the value and standards that meet the expectations of their users. This level of maturity which starts from the customer and ends with the product in the customers' hands, to empower them to meet their own needs, ensures that the business works together through the necessary practice of close, focused collaboration with combined goals to ensure that they continue to sustain and strengthen their position in the market.

Develop the product

Product development is the overall process of taking a product, solution, or service from concept through design, creation, customization, and into the customers' hands.

We have a product that exists either as an idea or a physical asset. We recognize that this asset will significantly benefit our target market and ultimately increase our organization's revenue—so we invest in it. This investment involves the ongoing transformation of the product as we continue to grow our market share and consumers realize the value we provide. The product is developed from its Minimum Viable state with teams across the business engaged in redefining the roadmap, delivering features, marketing, and sales—ultimately enabling greater customer value. The product continues to iterate through user feedback and changing market needs.

Product development or engineering is responsible for the technical creation and continuous evolution of the product. Nearing the end of its development, the marketing team can come on board to develop a Go-To-Market (GTM) process for unveiling a new product or new features. Marketing and sales tend to work in close collaboration to define the GTM strategy and ensure they align efforts to attract and win new deals and drive market adoption. The GTM strategy typically includes details of the target audience, marketing plan, pricing strategy, and messaging.

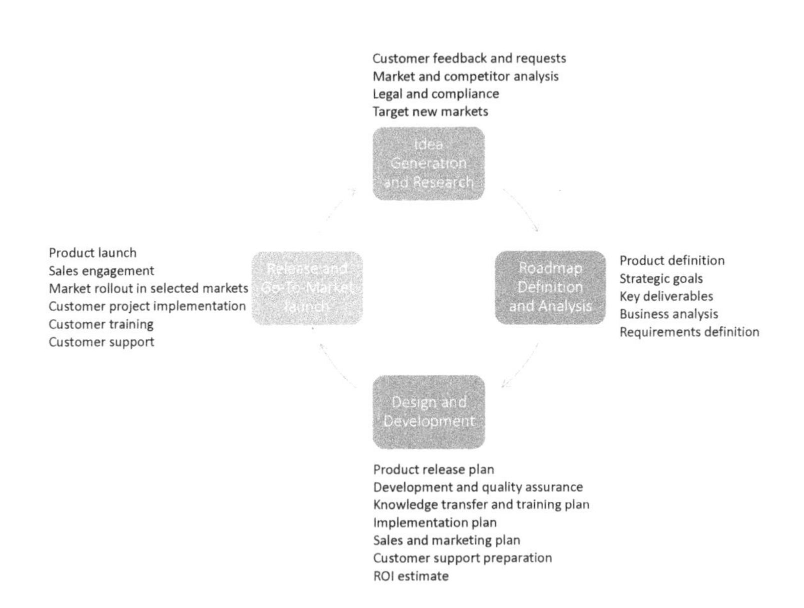

Around this time, teams from other areas of the business can re-engage. Each may now begin to learn about the product to support the release activity and customer engagement actions. More likely than not, each team will be operating in silos and rushing to get ready for the product release. If the product is a cloud solution with frequent releases, these departments will find themselves playing catch up if they are not well prepared. The result of this last-minute preparation is that the rest of the business will not be fully ready to support the customer, who will suffer from a poor adoption experience. The more frequently a product evolves, the more challenging it becomes for the organization to maintain a coordinated approach to taking a solution to its target market.

Choose the delivery process

Over the years, numerous approaches to delivering software have been practiced, including the Waterfall model, Agile, Lean, Dynamic Systems Development Method (DSDM), and Rational Unified Process (RUP).

The Waterfall model is the more traditional process that is characterized by its well-defined sequence of stage gates. These stages are broadly, divided into Requirements, Planning, Design, Development, Quality Assurance, and Launch. Each phase must be completed before the process moves to the next step, with no opportunity to return to the previous stage. Project timelines are based on each of the stages and are defined upfront. If one stage takes longer to complete, it has a knock-on effect on subsequent stages, and later stages are likely to be impacted.

At each stage of a Waterfall project, different teams will take responsibility for moving the project forward. So, for instance, at the requirements stage, business analysts will typically spend weeks or longer writing detailed specifications documents with the expectation that the developers who will undertake the work will understand every requirement in sufficient detail to deliver the solution. Business analysts might work with customers and stakeholders to define the requirements for how the solutions and systems will be implemented. Once the documents are reviewed and approved, software architects and developers will accept the specifications and begin the effort to read the documentation to begin design and development. It's possible at this stage that there will be several revisions of the requirements specification where questions and feedback arise and require clarification. These revisions need to be reviewed and passed through the approval process.

During the design and development stage, software engineers focus their efforts on building the solution. They may discover that they need additional resources, technologies, or tools, or uncover unaccounted complexities. It might also be that not all the skills required exist within the team. Figuring out these challenges at this stage can lead to further delays, moving out the timeline set for development.

Eventually, the development is done, and the developers have the approval to pass the completed work to the quality team for testing. Unfortunately, time might be a bit short as the testing may now have started later than planned due to previous delays. If there are delays, the project manager and stakeholders worry about missing delivery dates, so it's left to the testers not to let the entire project fail. Now under pressure, they need to understand the project's requirements and the solution that the developers have built so that they can prepare their tests.

Reading through requirements and design documents and asking for clarification from the business analysts and the development team takes time. Then, when the testing starts, it might be that the developed solution doesn't completely fit the specification or that several defects need to be fixed. So, there is a back-and-forth between the testers, analysts, and developers. For each defect, a cycle of fix, approval, and re-test is required. Time is short, and the pressure is on, so there is a trade-off between time and quality.

Typically, timescales that are defined and committed to the business at the early stages of the project will change as delays happen through each waterfall phase. The initial requirements might introduce scope creep or misalignment as the project moves along. With teams operating in silos with poor communication, as deadlines loom, the testing effort, which comes at the end of the project, will be compromised due to the fixed deadline. Unfortunately, the customer, the recipient of the final product, may end up with a solution that falls short of their expectations.

The Waterfall method, originally used in the construction and manufacturing industries, is rigid and heavily process-driven, which allows for costly mistakes. In fact, software project failures have been attributed to the lack of flexibility in its linear approach to moving projects through phases without opportunities to revisit work done in previous stages. As the market continues to change rapidly, there needs to be flexibility in the way businesses manage priorities and the speed with which they can provide solutions for their customers. This method will be problematic for large, complex projects or environments where frequent change is the norm. However, the Waterfall method is still well suited for projects where the requirements are well-defined and understood and are unlikely to change. Without collaboration and alignment across the business, this method is difficult to apply effectively. I believe this is partly the reason why it is looked upon negatively in the software industry. Setting out fixed timescales over long periods from the start is a recipe for failure. However, this can be achieved over shorter periods where the path is well understood. So, there are still situations in which the Waterfall method is applicable.

Enter Agile

Agile is an iterative framework aimed at delivering value early in the product development cycle. The idea is to deliver early and frequently to gain feedback from users on the feature being developed before it is fully mature. This approach helps to identify sooner whether the effort is worth the investment. Many organizations adopt Agile with the hope of delivering their solutions faster to shorten the time to market, manage change, and improve quality.

The framework is based on a well-defined set of values, principles, and practices. Agile practices rely on cross-functional teams working together to deliver products and services in short cycles, understanding that the customer receives the highest value early before all the requirements and functionality have been completely built. Changes are incrementally incorporated into the build process, allowing for more frequent opportunities for feedback cycles and for changes to be incorporated into each iteration so that higher value features will emerge much sooner.

Agile, and *Scrum* in particular, aims to eliminate silos by motivating multi-disciplinary individuals to work together through time-boxed sprints. Customers and stakeholders are involved in the development process early and are more likely to receive the value they require. The development team can use an inspect and adapt approach for continuous improvement. This flexible approach also helps build trust with customers engaged with early visibility and input into the product's features, leading to a more successful outcome.

One of the main aims in Agile is that autonomous, self-organizing teams can identify roadblocks and issues that occurred during a sprint to resolve them quickly while continuously inspecting how they performed at each iteration. This allows the teams to iterate with product features and continuous cycles of process improvements, allowing them to deliver more efficiently and effectively. Scrum is an Agile framework designed for delivering software through faster feedback loops, continuous improvement, and the ability to respond rapidly to change.

There are, however, some disadvantages to scrum, in that a team working in sprints is not easily able to break away from the scrum cycle. How or when does the team find room for broader innovation or for improving individual skills? How does an Agile team manage technical debt or experiment with different working methods when they are expected to work continuously against a release train they are measured on? Scrum is aimed at software development, but what about the rest of the organization? It becomes more challenging when the engineering team frequently delivers through an Agile framework while the rest of the business continues to work in a typical waterfall method.

In both Waterfall and Agile, product development teams can find themselves falling into functional silos even though they are all working towards the same ultimate goal. This can lead to problems where dependencies crop up, misunderstandings occur between teams that fail to align, and delays or confusion might occur over which team takes ownership for certain work items. Breaking down silos completely, narrowing boundaries, and creating cross-functional teams in an organization will allow for better, faster project implementations.

Scaled Agile Framework - SAFe

In 2011, the Scaled Agile Framework, or SAFe, was introduced. In a nutshell, it aims to scale Agile across the enterprise, introducing greater alignment between teams towards the same overarching business goals. It addresses a disconnected, siloed delivery mechanism by enabling cross-functional teams to work together across the enterprise, operating within the same iteration cycles.

SAFe is most applicable to enterprise organizations wanting to achieve business agility, where there are organizational and operational complexities. The framework contains a collection of patterns and best industry practices organized around the seven core competencies of Lean Agile leadership, team and technical agility, Agile product delivery, enterprise solution delivery, lean portfolio management, organizational agility, and a continuous learning culture. Taking elements of Lean and Agile, SAFe offers a customer-centric, scale-up approach where teams across the business form Agile release trains working on a continuous delivery pipeline. Since its inception, SAFe has grown significantly.

However, it's worth noting that some aspects of SAFe undermine core Agile principles. There is a lot of upfront planning and process required from the highest-level

Portfolio, which takes a top-down approach. It reduces the ability for individuals and teams to be autonomous and self-organizing and restricts their means to adapt to change more frequently. Decisions, including solution design, are made by high-level authorities who are furthest from the people who perform the implementation.

You may recall the story of the early days of mass production in the first part of this book. In the early days of Ford production, authorities far removed from the production line made decisions without the assembly teams' involvement. The assembly workers had little input into the design, process, or recommendations to improve the factory operations or tooling. The decisions made by higher-ups resulted in product and quality issues, and without a rapid feedback loop, resulted primarily in wasted efficiency and cost to the business.

On the other hand, Toyota realized that the ownership and engagement of their production workers were central to the success of the final product and, in particular, the loyalty and satisfaction of their customers. This approach led to the creation of Lean. SAFe, in its attempt to centrally scale up a business, appears, to a certain degree, to mirror some of the flaws of earlier models. However, it presents a mechanism for driving better alignment across large enterprises and allowing for the coordinated delivery of solutions to market.

The question thus remains unresolved: How can organizations do Agile at scale? How do Agile teams retain their own levels of autonomy while continuing to operate collectively to achieve the overarching business goals? The answer lies in simplicity and not layers of bureaucracy or top-down decision-making. Introducing layers of complexity and bureaucracy get in the way of progress by introducing unnecessary waste and reducing productivity. Instead, organizational goals must be well defined, easily understood, and achievable. Align teams with these common goals, and the environment should be organized in such a fashion that allows for facilitation, local accountability, broad collaboration, transparency, and continuous improvement at the team level and across the organization.

Principle 4 of the Agile Manifesto suggests that *business people and developers must work together daily throughout the project*. If I had to invest money, time and effort, it would be to improve business agility by creating a supportive culture where facilitators would be integrated into teams and measured by their ability to coach and mentor to reduce bottlenecks and roadblocks. The objectives of this role would be to create a broader culture aimed at putting the customer first, enabling teams across the organization to build stronger bridges and provide transparency. Collective buy-in means the organization can have visibility throughout the portfolio, quickly identify problems, and resolve them at every level.

When it comes to decision-making, this can be more effectively achieved by engaging directly with the delivery teams. It amazes me how organizations invest a great deal of time, effort, and money in attracting and recruiting the very best talent, only to bring them on board and fail to harness their creative and intellectual capability. This was the approach Toyota integrated into their company from the very early days: engaging their assembly staff in the decisions made about their production process and operations.

As Agile principles and values suggest, creating an environment where collaboration between individuals and interactions rules over processes and tools, removes boundaries, and allows for faster iterations, ensuring that customer satisfaction is prioritized by continuously providing valuable solutions in a constantly changing environment. Build projects in an environment of trust with motivated and empowered individuals where the standards and expectations are clear. In developing an Agile culture, organizations should not lose sight of the need to establish support, simplicity, and collaboration, which will bring out the best of their people for the long-term benefit of their customers and business. This does not mean that people are given the freedom to do whatever they want to do. Instead, there needs to be clear alignment and goals, with each person having an awareness of their role in bringing about the success of the business.

Companies should aim to resist the tendency for cookie cutting in their attempt to measure all teams in exactly the same way, form, and function. It isn't that simple—humans aren't that simple and neither are technology projects. In most cases, the contexts will vary, from team to team, product to product. Organizations that use tools to compare and measure every engineering team in the same way to identify areas of weakness indicate a top-down concern in which senior leadership lacks trust in their people and possibly their own lack of confidence in their ability to lead their teams.

Product development teams are individuals working together to build valuable systems and solutions. Typically, the teams form as a combination of product managers, business analysts, architects, user experience designers, quality analysts, security engineers, and software engineers. These cross-functional teams will collaborate with the business to gather requirements and work towards well-defined quality and success criteria. "How do we know if the product meets the requirement?" "Who are our end-users and how will they interact with the system?" The answers to these questions will allow teams to develop empathy and further understand how to build the right solution that meets the needs of their market. Beyond just churning out code, the team needs to self-organize to design and deliver the right product, which requires them to have a greater sense of collective ownership. Most importantly, the team needs to continuously identify errors and mistakes, learn from them and take actions to improve.

There is a lot of talk and focus on Agile these days. Some people treat it as a religion, and others know that it is just another tool to facilitate product delivery. In my role as an engineering leader, and for over a decade, I have led several Agile transformation programs of delivery teams both in the case of co-located teams and more expansively across global organizations with distributed teams. The effort required to conduct a successful transformation is by no means easy or for the faint-hearted, but the outcomes have been extremely fulfilling.

Agility is a mindset, and the change requires not just the need to restructure people and roles, but also fundamentally, to support them through an emotional journey that requires empathy, hand-holding, and certainly coaching individuals. The objective is to inspire people to adapt to Agile principles in which the customer is key, transparency is all-important, collaboration is the way to accelerate productivity and alignment through conversations, and continuous inspection and improvement is the means to adapt and become a better version of yesterday. Suppose teams can achieve all of these—something I have witnessed numerous times—and are given the autonomy to become truly self-organizing, self-reflecting, and self-correcting. In that case, they will be capable of consistently achieving their goals through increased productivity cycles while eliminating wasteful practices from their ways of working.

My advice to businesses is not to get fixated on the Agile framework as a key driver for achieving business goals but rather to treat it as a facilitation tool. Remember that your ultimate aim is to deliver value to customers, not story points, velocity, or pretty dashboards. Finally, Agile should not be a means to introduce heavyweight processes that will drown your teams' efforts. As with the Lean method, the measure of success lies in the ability to deliver the highest customer value to the desired quality standards while progressively identifying mechanisms to reduce waste. Measuring waste frequently to make improvements and reduce costs will also drive greater efficiencies, which will move the business closer to increased productivity, predictability, and consistency. Key to this is supporting opportunities with greater collaboration, transparency, continuous improvement, and alignment of the strategic vision and goals.

Optimization is a major step towards improved and sophisticated methods of delivering products. Teams can gather data throughout the delivery cycle and through various reviews and identify opportunities to improve and accelerate the process. Take, for example, an Agile team that operates each sprint as a mini waterfall method. Scoping of requirements is completed, which allows the developers to conduct their design and start development. Once the software is ready, the testers write their test cases and proceed to execute them. Then when bugs are raised, they return to the developers to fix—rinse and repeat. Now, this is a sequential approach.

So, what if you could speed this up? Introducing parallel flows becomes more efficient by establishing a design phase where the UX designers, software engineers, and test engineers conduct designs of their wireframes, technical designs, and test cases. Peer review happens around the same time within the team, and then the development and test efforts begin. Testing will involve the set up of data and environments and the creation of automation tests. When the development is completed, the code is executed against the tests, anticipating that tests are ready. Quick and early feedback ensures that defects are picked up and corrected, allowing the release to be delivered in a fraction of the original time.

We can optimize this process even further. During the requirements and scoping phase, with the team closely collaborating through discussions and discovery, UX and technical design and test case definition occur around the same time, so essentially, the teams are scoping and designing in sync. Spikes for the larger or complex unknowns are carried out to clarify the feasibility of implementing the feature. This allows for any adjustments at the early stage of delivery. The teams align with their understanding of the work required, so allowing them to proceed to development and test execution quickly. In doing this, they move to a faster, more optimized delivery cadence.

In establishing mature delivery processes, a combination of practices is necessary. The entire organization, not just the delivery teams, is engaged in fully integrated Agile and lean practices, focusing on achieving the key strategic goals successfully. As we have already identified, mature practices incorporate optimizations through continuous improvement cycles where they are always looking for opportunities to eliminate waste to accelerate and be more productive.

CHAPTER 5

Software Engineering

I don't believe we can talk about software engineering in the commercial sense without thinking customer-first.

In my earlier years when I was a technical team leader at a large corporation that dominated its market, our CEO invited several of our customers to speak at our company's annual conference. He wanted us to hear what they had to say about their customer experiences. Why did he ask for this? Because our competitors were gaining ground and we were starting to lose market share. What our customers told us came as a surprise. The message wasn't about praise and thanks to our business. On the contrary, they told us that although they valued the service we provided, we were also arrogant. In short, they explained that we did not take the time to understand their problems and their needs and that we tended to deliver solutions to them that we thought were for their good, but that wasn't necessarily so. This message had a profound impact throughout my career in terms of how I think and make decisions. It happened at a time before the word *Agile* was even mentioned.

What lesson did this feedback teach us? As a business, we all felt the message and took it on board. The CEO was clearly a smart person — if you don't hear it from me, you can hear it from our users. We acted. Fast. We looked at the approach we took for the engineering organization to deliver solutions to our customers and saw just how internalized we were. We formed working groups of which I was actively engaged to redefine our entire end-to-end engineering processes. We changed our waterfall methodology from being stage-gate driven to being customer-focused and more collaborative. From the initial requirements scoping, we would meet with customers, often at their premises, to conduct discovery and storyboarding exercises, understand their problems, and gather their feedback. We worked on the solution together too.

We tailored those inputs into our products. We embarked on customer field trials with willing participants: a formal process to enable our customers to have early hands-on alpha or beta versions for feedback before product completion and release. And once the product was released, we would visit our customers to listen to their experience with the new solution and learn how they managed their operations. We listened and empathized. And so, we learned to understand our customers more and fine-tuned the solutions they wanted. Overall, we saw an increase in the levels of trust and satisfaction we enjoyed with our customers.

Since the software crisis in the 1960s, which saw largely problematic software practices leading to expensive failures, efforts have been made to mature engineering practices. However, we still have a long way to go to achieve the desired level of maturity. Very rarely will one encounter any two organizations that practice a standardized, consistent, or predictable software delivery methods. In addition, job roles vary widely in responsibilities and levels of seniority, and no format can match a role in one organization with the same in another. The trouble with this lack of a standardized approach suggests that people, practices, and the end product will differ widely. Efforts have been made to define standard job roles and levels through training and certification, formal qualifications, or proven levels of competence—but they are sporadic and have failed to achieve the desired impact.

Building software revolves around a range of practices, including requirements definition, planning, design, development, testing, documentation, deployment, and maintenance. Teams must work together from beginning to end to be effective in building software. I recommend that they engage in a stakeholder mapping exercise to define clear lines of communication, needs, and dependencies while producing a responsibility assignment matrix or RACI. This will provide a better understanding of who should be consulted and informed and to what extent.

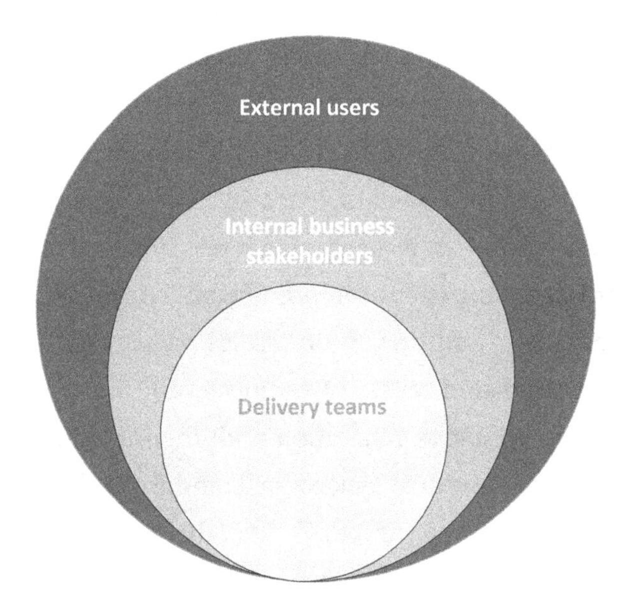

Broadly speaking, science is a discipline that studies the natural world to explain its occurrence. More specifically, applied science or general engineering takes existing scientific knowledge and develops practical applications through a systemic approach. Technology has an interdependent relationship with science and engineering. Science acts as a source of new knowledge to provide ideas and innovations for advances in human life or to meet new social needs. It also provides tools and techniques that can improve design efficiencies in engineering and information to support research and development.

Software engineering is a discipline concerned with the processes, methods, and tooling necessary to design, implement and manage software to the desired quality standard. General engineering practices incorporate computer science and mathematics principles. The production of software requires applying practices related to the software language, code, and its construct. Developers hone their skills around implementing and modifying programming languages—languages often abstracted from their underlying physical assets.

When we look back at the history of programming languages, it started with assembly language, a low-level language documented specifically for a machine. Written instructions are converted into executable code, which sends instructions directly to the machine's architecture. This required detailed knowledge of a specific computer was non-portable, slow to implement, hard to maintain, and intellectually laborious. Then came compiled languages with the source code being translated into machine-language instructions. This made it easier to develop software that was independent of the computer hardware. The arrival of cloud computing created further distance for developers who could focus more on providing software as a service and meant they were less concerned with physical computer networks.

As technologies advance, we are moving to a paradigm where the physical world will play a more prominent role in how software is applied. Today, we can deliver the same software solution across multiple devices such as mobile, web, and smart wearables. For each of these platforms, considerations need to be determined for how the software is optimized for that environment. Now, more than ever, we also need to be concerned with the performance of software on an increasing array of hardware platforms such as physical sensors, medical equipment, plant and automation, and visual monitoring and tracking systems which require real-time data collection with the ability to gather insights and turn them into action, all without human intervention. Coupled with this is the growing need for interoperability between multiple devices and systems, and integration of data from multiple sources.

This growing industry requires newly adapted skills where hardware and software engineers cross their boundaries of knowledge - hardware engineers develop software engineering know-how, and software engineers harness physical machinery and components expertise.

Those successful engineers will have the ability to expand their skills in developing innovative services for applications that sit on multiple devices, platforms, and systems. This new environment will require hardware, software, and automation engineers, and data analysts and security experts working in close collaboration. To do this effectively will require new standards for processes, practices, and methods of working to deliver complex, secure solutions for the technological landscape. The industry will also need to develop new standards and tooling for quality, certification, and compliance. Engineering skills that cross the boundaries of software and hardware to form the intersection are likely to be in high demand as the industry forges ahead. Understanding how to optimize performance and embed secure, reliable and resilient software will be key proponents of maturity for the technology practices.

Automation is key to how quickly a business can scale. The more you standardize, the greater the opportunity to automate, allowing faster growth with reduced long-term costs, freeing up efforts to focus on future growth.

Begin with quality

Can we talk about a "product" without mentioning quality? Some lessons learned from manufacturing and other mature industries are that standardization, quality standards, and waste reduction help businesses accelerate their product deliveries while maintaining relatively lower costs.

Quality touches every aspect of the delivery chain, ensuring that when the end-user gets their hands on the solution, they are satisfied with the outcome. In engineering terms, quality applies from the initial requirements. In building out the product, we're working towards meeting the expected standards required by the consumer.

The earlier you build quality into the product, the less overhead you will have to contend with maintenance, technical debt, and defect management. There are often debates and tensions over how much effort you put into quality practices during product development. Some believe that investment in quality equals time wasted and delays to market. These beliefs emerge from a sense of urgency to deliver more features to market quickly for fear of losing out on market share and revenue, suggesting that trade-offs are necessary. Indeed, the sense of urgency exists, and pragmatically, trade-offs will always happen.

However, where do you draw the line? How much effort do you need to invest in delivering a qualitative solution before your customers become frustrated? In any industry, risks are likely, and your market's appetite should drive the measure of calculated risks that you're willing to consume. The good news is that there are approaches to take that allow teams to deliver fast, frequent releases of satisfactory quality.

What makes a good quality product comes down to the needs of the industry and customers' attitudes to those standards in that industry. The aviation industry, for instance, demands strict standards of compliance for quality and safety, defined by the Civil Aviation Authority. On the other end of the scale, a social media application can typically release changes daily, understanding that the output will include more acceptable defects. Users are more tolerant of bugs because they most likely won't have to wait too long for the next update. One of these industries is operationally critical to life, while the other can withstand far more risk.

There are various quality maturity models, of which TMMi, or the Test Maturity Model Integration is the most popular. TMMi looks at different stages of testing within organizations, from the ad hoc, unstructured approach to the more mature stage in which testing is a means of prevention, followed by quality control and optimization processes.

Within any industry, the testing methods employed by a business will depend on the standards required by its market and the industry. To progress to more mature quality assurance practices, organizations will be required to move towards a well-defined, measured, and optimized process, promoting improved productivity and reductions in cost. Where do you perceive your company is with its quality maturity processes?

Level	Description
Level 1 Unstructured	An organization uses ad hoc, unstructured methods for testing; results are not repeatable and there is no documented quality standard.
Level 2 Managed	Testing is defined as a documented and repeatable process. Test strategies, test plans, and test cases exist based on requirements. Testing usually begins late in the software development lifecycle.
Level 3 Defined	The test process is integrated into a software lifecycle from the requirements gathering stage. Knowledge and best practices are shared among colleagues. Training is provided to improve skills.
Level 4 Measured	Testing activities take place at all stages of the software lifecycle, from requirements and designs through release. Quality criteria are agreed upon and evaluated. Peer reviews take place across the lifecycle. Monitoring and measurement are part of the process.
Level 5 Optimization	The organization proactively prevents defects. The testing process itself is tested and improved iteratively. Test teams strive to optimize their process through continuous improvement to achieve faster testing, time to market, and reduced waste. Quality controls are in place.

Product Testing

Introducing quality practices from the earliest point in the software development lifecycle is known to help reduce waste, cost, time, and effort. Traditionally, and it still is the mindset in some areas of the software industry, quality is considered the responsibility of a group of experts called testers or quality assurance engineers. This practice has its beginnings in the waterfall methodology, where the last stage of delivering software was testing. We know that this is an expensive process that delays and brings about complexity through potential rework.

Define a high-level quality strategy for the guiding principles on addressing quality systematically throughout the product lifecycle. Once this is defined, it must be communicated and distributed across the organization and incorporated into development, release, and support processes. This is a long-term action plan on how quality standards will be achieved to satisfy the customer's needs. The strategy should not be static and should be kept alive with regular reviews and ongoing improvements.

Quality through the Product Lifecycle

Discovery and scope - The WHAT

Understanding what is needed and why to create the desired solution is necessary for alignment across product teams. Effort done at this stage will save money and reduce overhead later. Unclear requirements create misunderstandings, leading to flaws in the product. Equally, verbose documentation is an expensive waste of time for the author and those who have to read it to understand what is required to create the solution. You might have come across software that has been poorly developed due to a misunderstanding of the requirements. In more extreme cases, poorly documented requirements will lead developers to make costly guesses of their own and potentially extend scope by defining new scenarios.

To enhance the process of defining clear requirements without writing lengthy documentation, a desired approach introduces a collaborative effort. The product owner, domain experts, developers, and testers discuss and share the same context in defining "What if" scenarios and examples. This will help bring everyone on board to define concrete examples upfront and provide the means for defining test cases and methods much earlier in the delivery process. This early-stage qualitative approach will offer greater context and clarity about the desired solution for the design and build phases. Useful techniques known as Specification by Example and Behavioral Driven Development (BDD) can help to speed up the requirements and test definition process. We will cover these methods later.

Technical discovery is an important component of this stage. Too often, teams under pressure to get started rush into developing the solution quickly instead of investing valuable time in a technical assessment or feasibility activity. Teams do not invest enough time in discovery, leading to failures and delays later in the delivery cycle. Uncovering complexities and unknowns during development, instead of identifying them earlier on during discovery, means wasting time due to further detailed analysis, scoping, and substantial rework. During technical discovery, high-level solution design takes place to understand further the approach required to develop the solution. Any unknown or complex features may require prototyping, which Agile teams may describe as spikes. These are typically timeboxed activities. Clarification and further analysis might be required and will need to be fed into the scoping exercise. The idea here is to identify and address risks, provide a clearer definition of the technical solution and the means to deliver it, and ensure that previously unclear requirements have been refined. The output of this activity will be a high-level technical design specification.

Wireframes, user flows, and storyboard designs are invaluable for defining how users interact with the product. User testing will help validate the concept and confirm whether the feature or solution will achieve its goals. Collaborative efforts at this stage will produce a toolbox with a well-defined scope in the form of user stories, a high-level design specification, and user-experience wireframes, all of which provide the necessary detail to kick off the delivery effort. Estimates derived at this stage will be more realistic and give a better chance of a successful solution implementation. They also present an opportunity for discussions over scope, time, or resources when time or deadlines are a constraint.

Design, develop, and test - The HOW

Before development starts, more detail is needed on scope. In Agile terms, this is where epics are broken down into stories, along with design and test artifacts.

A more detailed technical design will be required to assess how the solution should be implemented and provide the occasion for engineers to discuss and review the most appropriate approaches, having factored in risks, technology requirements, skills, capabilities, and levels of complexity. As with requirements, it is important to understand how the solution should be built within the team. Design documents and checklists help guide the work and ensure that considerations in key areas have been taken into account. Peer design reviews with subject matter experts help evaluate how the design will achieve requirements through a feedback cycle that ensures that risks are addressed early. My advice is to keep design documents as lightweight as possible and focus on risks and key areas that need context and clarity.

I have often found that not enough effort and consideration is given to both development and test case designs. This is partly because engineers are often under pressure to start developing code or might fail to value the importance of investing time upfront in defining the implementation details required to deliver a solution. It also helps validate the technical feasibility of a solution and identify any risks that might hamper the ability to satisfy the requirements. Moving ahead on the product solution without enough attention will likely lead to misalignment and expensive mistakes, with flaws appearing in the solution later in the process. Designs are a communication tool for engineers to understand the requirements and have a shared vision of the development approach.

Testing strategies

During delivery, test validation at every stage ensures that the product meets a set of quality standards. Quality is an area that requires consistency and standardization across the tech industry, much like it features in mature industries. A product should be easy to maintain and extend to not degrade existing features' quality. Where errors and failures occur, the product will need to respond gracefully and share informative feedback to the user, so the user still feels in control of the situation until the product returns to normal operation. Some products may have to manage high volume demands, large numbers of users or may need to handle peak traffic at specific times of the year, all while operating without downtime. Where parts of the system are complex or prone to error, pay special attention to ensure that accidental modifications don't introduce defects that might be difficult to diagnose and fix.

Testing software is non-trivial, with efforts made to ensure that the product's internals can be tested in a way that protects it from changes that might compromise its integrity. Attempting to provide full testing coverage is usually unnecessary and will likely take up a lot of time and effort. It is important to assess the impact of a change and the likelihood of failure occurring before determining how much effort is worth investing in tests. A risk-based approach to testing is efficient in terms of where time is dedicated.

A lightweight test plan will help determine what features need to be tested and the methods and techniques required. Good practice requires a culture of peer reviews by team members and business users close to the product, not just the test team. Test cases define the actual tests that need to be carried out. If an initial test specification was carried out efficiently during the requirements stage, it would support the efforts to define further tests in detail. It is, however, important to call out that the main objective here is to define what needs testing to identify as many defects as possible in the product before it is released. Testing covers many different facets, and it's important to pay the necessary attention and effort to the right areas.

In the past, white box and black box testing have been the standard approaches to validation. Simply put, white box testing is the internal, low-level unit testing of functions and methods that validate the product's behavior, logic, and integrity. These are the tests written by the software engineers to test the system's inner workings and ensure that errors can quickly be surfaced and diagnosed in case of failure. Black box tests validate the product's functionality with no knowledge of the internal logic and depend on the tester providing a set of inputs to the system to verify the output. Functional automated tests will help proactively identify defects introduced as early on as possible in the product during development, and being automated, will save many hours of time and effort.

Test coverage

What constitutes good test cases? Positive or 'happy path' testing is the most popular and applied means of addressing quality through requirements, design, and implementation. This form validates the correctness of a feature's methods and functionality. It is a good start but by itself is insufficient. Other forms of testing should involve negative, boundary, and equivalent conditions. We need to test the system for when things go wrong and to ensure that it responds adequately. We also need to ensure that existing functionality behaves as defined and has not been broken by a change. Boundary tests are applied where values may exceed specific conditions, which are likely to cause a failure. In those cases, we should check that the system can operate responsibly.

Several tools measure test coverage at various levels of testing. Coverage has tended to be a measure of quality in which teams aim to test the system to a high percentage. The problem with blindly applying test coverage as a measure is that we might find ourselves investing a significant amount of time, effort, and resources with relatively minimal gain, or we might be applying the wrong type of testing that could obscure key areas that require more attention. This is where risk-based testing comes in. Risk-based testing presents a probabilistic approach to quality assurance, which assesses and defines the likelihood of the risk of a defect or undesirable outcome based on frequency, complexity, criticality, threats, and impact. This practice helps teams prioritize the time and effort spent on quality assurance while ensuring that they can continue optimizing their output.

Quality methods

Functional and non-functional testing methods form part of a product's quality strategy. As well as testing the behavior of the solution, it is also important to test how the product performs as a system within its environment. One of the main reasons we test is to make sure that the product works as expected and safeguards going forward. When we create extensions or make changes, it will still be expected to behave according to specification.

When it comes to testing the functions of the product, we make sure that we write unit tests to validate the internal, low-level methods of the product to a level of coverage that developers can measure. The other functional tests, including integration, regression, smoke, user interface, end-to-end, and user acceptance, should be included in your suite of testing methods, and possibly localization, compliance, and even cultural testing.

From a system perspective, non-functional tests will validate how well the system performs, scales, handles traffic and volume, load and stress, and errors or failure conditions. Users of a piece of software, especially when it is business critical, need to trust that it is dependable and will work correctly, as expected. The reliability of the software, which is running without failure, will need to be measured and validated. It is better to focus on improved reliability instead of maintenance or defect management.

In other words, being proactive by preventing failures rather than having to react to fixing them.

Take cybersecurity as an example. Malware and cyber-attacks have increased over the years, and key targets, such as military computers and government systems, have been compromised. Attacks on systems are increasing, and distributed denial of service (DDoS) attacks frequently cause outages. These events and ransomware activities where vulnerabilities are detected and exploited, often result in data breaches, severe disruption, distractions, and financial hijacking. Until recently, businesses have tended to treat security as a unit separate and not integral to their operations. It is no surprise that hackers, knowing this, can act swiftly to identify vulnerabilities and take advantage of them. With the rise of cybersecurity threats, awareness is growing that security concerns must be core to every business. This is not just the requirement of technical and technology functions, but rather that there is an awareness and responsibility of every individual within the organization.

In July 2020, Garmin, the fitness smartwatch maker and service provider, was hit by a ransomware attack that forced the shutdown of its website, call centers, and online services. This left customers unable to connect data on their fitness devices with their online accounts or access their health data. Pilots using Garmin for managing their flight plans were also impacted. WastedLocker, a sophisticated ransomware software, was deployed by cyber attackers onto the Garmin platform, with the sole aim to encrypt and therefore hijack files, making them unrecoverable and resulting in their major outage. In the end, Garmin was forced to pay a yet unconfirmed amount of money for their encrypted files to be released.

In December 2020, the systems of US federal agencies and tech companies such as Microsoft were compromised by an indirect cyber-attack. However, in March, the series of events began earlier that year when malicious software was stealthily updated onto network-monitoring software made by a vendor called SolarWinds. This allowed the hackers to piggyback off Orion. This SolarWinds software solution is sold to large corporations and government agencies worldwide and extracts sensitive information from multiple networks and systems.

These are only a few examples of the extent of the cybersecurity threat, and right now, security prevention and detection are essential. In your product organization, perhaps the software development lifecycle, or SDLC, needs to be extended to the SSDLC, the Secure Software Development Lifecycle, as a process for managing risk and building secure software applications from the ground up. Each stage of software development covers secure practices from design right through to release. Teams involved in delivering software — and this impacts all parts of the business, not only the technical teams — must have awareness and ownership of secure practices. However, thorough risk-based testing does not stop there. The suppliers and providers of third parties must also form part of the ongoing security due diligence conducted by the business. How third-party tools are sourced, upgraded, and integrated into an organization's products and services must be subject to strict guidelines, rules, and practices.

When it comes to developing software, the scope definition should incorporate the requirements necessary for a secure solution. Working with your internal security team, understanding standards such as OWASP (Open Source Foundation for Application Security), and regulatory compliance requirements for your customers should help define the expectations necessary to create a more secure product or solution. Secure software ensures only authorized users can access it, while the integrity of the data, and unauthorized threats are prevented.

Identifying and assessing potential threats at the design stage is called threat modeling and allows taking steps to address the risks. From the design stage through the development and release pipelines, security requirements must be implemented and validated. Various forms of validation will include the continuous scanning of software and third-party tools along with penetration testing, which can help identify vulnerabilities. The idea behind the principle of least privilege is that any user, program, or process can have only the bare minimum privileges necessary to perform its function. Minimizing a user's access for just what is required can dramatically reduce security risks and attack surfaces.

Develop software with these principles in mind. Some questions to ask as you design your software are:

- How can we allow system administrators to easily implement the principle of least privilege?
- How easily can an intruder get access to your backend systems and data?
- If they did access your data, how meaningful or valuable will it be to them?
- How exposed is your API logic and documentation?
- How are your transfers and endpoint parameters secured?
- Have you thought about encryption through your application and where you store your authentication, authorization, and encryption keys?
- What is your strategy for managing secure sessions?

Many questions need to be formulated and analyzed during the architecture and design, development, and testing stages to ensure that security risks are significantly decreased long before the application goes live.

Your stakeholders in this process are those accountable for security in your organization. They are kept up to date with regular changes to the ever-evolving security landscape. They will need to be working closely with product development teams to share expectations, review designs, and guide efforts on quality assurance. Even better still is to restructure teams to incorporate security champions whose role is to drive awareness, capability, and best security practices.

When it comes to the user experience, how well would you say you know your customer? What drives their business and productivity? What challenges do they face day-to-day? How your customers engage with your product should be well understood by the various functions of your business. Until recently, user experience was considered an afterthought during the development process, and the person developing the software had to come up with a 'clever' way for the user to interact with the product. This led to many inconsistencies in different parts of the same product and has created frustrations amongst users, often causing loss of productivity in businesses.

The role of a user experience (UX) designer is relatively new to the software industry and, thankfully, is now becoming mainstream in many businesses. The right product with a seamless UX can make a significant improvement to the way a business operates. More mature business practices incorporate UX throughout their delivery cycles from the first point of ideation and design through development and testing. I have known products which have been ruled out of the sales process due to their outdated look-and-feel, or lack of user friendliness.

UX design involves user research, prototyping, and high-level design during the requirements gathering phase and product trials with real users. User research requires that the UX designer engages with all users, internal and external, to their organization. The product and system's visual and interactive designs will be drawn to enhance the team's scope during development. The designer will need to support the engineers and carry out UX testing during the build stage. Ideally, user experience assessments with stakeholders and customers should be conducted as part of a feedback loop to gather data and make improvements.

Onboarding a new product in any business requires an investment, not just in terms of financial cost, but also in implementing a change within the organization and the time and effort required for their people to achieve fluency. This change is likely to have an initial impact on productivity and business performance. Take, for instance, that your target market comprises mostly large enterprises whose users have to manage highly complex processes, multiple transactions, and large volumes of data. They will need the ability to quickly and efficiently work with a solution that will facilitate this process. Having to execute multiple mouse clicks or large workflows to navigate around a screen or through the product can waste hours of productive time and frustrate the user. In addition, you want to improve your user's experience to have a positive perception and remain loyal customers.

How effectively end-users can use, learn, or control the system is central to their product experience. Ultimately, they need to feel that the system, as a tool, helps them to fulfill their needs in a way that appears seamless and intuitive. There's nothing worse than wasting time trying to figure out how to initiate, follow through, or complete an action and not know whether it turned out successful or not.

A user experience that is familiar, consistent, informative, and predictable goes a long way towards providing a high level of satisfaction. One of several ways to test out the product is to look at how each user type or persona interacts with the product and how well they can achieve their particular goals. As new features are added, or existing ones are altered, the application should be widely validated to ensure consistency in the visual cues you provide to your users. For instance, does color or text signal the same behavior or message, and can the user perform the same related actions or events throughout the application? Where messages are displayed, is there similar and well-understood language and structure? Setting UX guidelines will help drive a more consistent look-and-feel of the product. In addition, guidelines will help drive design, development, and testing. Better still, If you can build automated UI tests around these guidelines, this will help identify areas that fall below standard.

The effort to define the positive, 'happy path' of a feature is often more than identifying the negative failure scenarios. How a product responds to faults and failures is an important aspect of the user experience. Will the error response be graceful and flawless, or will it result in catastrophic shut-down? This can make a huge difference to the user's productivity and levels of stress. When errors or faults happen, how quickly can the system provide useful context and help bring about a quick resolution to reduce disruption?

Consider what information can be presented to the user in a format that helps them feel in control of the situation. It should be tailored to each particular user type and be relevant and easy to understand. For instance, for a particular fault, the detail that can help a user diagnose and potentially resolve the situation might be displayed differently, depending on factors such as their user profile, authorization level, and technical competency.

In mapping out 'the user,' we need to consider the situation more broadly than just the end-user. Every touchpoint of the product from within the business to the end-user has specific requirements to be addressed. For instance, the consultants who need to install or customize the product for their particular customers will need to understand the product's new features and provide a seamless installation or upgrade for the customer to have a system to use within a defined timescale. Those that have to train customers with new functionality will need to understand how the features work. Finally, the customer services consultants who will support the product once it goes live will need to be familiar with its features, any potential system weaknesses, and how to handle errors should they occur. Each represents a different type of user with different sets of requirements. To provide a compelling end-user experience, all participants in the support chain will also need to incorporate their requirements into the product delivery cycle.

A customer's experience with a product doesn't end when they receive it. This is just the beginning of their journey. The product needs to be straightforward to install and configure, easy and intuitive to work with. When things go wrong during its operation, they should receive timely feedback and assistance to minimize the impact. Design software to provide various means of support through real-time user feedback, diagnostics, logging, and tracing of information, the ability to heal or recover successfully, or to degrade in the face of a destructive incident gracefully. During the requirements gathering process, colleagues whose work is to install, configure, and support customers can provide input on how they expect the product to be supported and capable of smoothing the installation process. Knowing how the system will better support various customer environments will help them provide a better experience for their customers.

So your product is successful in the market, and demand continues to grow. As customer numbers expand and usage increases, you soon find that performance starts to become a problem. Your analysis shows that traffic to several servers is at an all-time high, leading to slow responsiveness or timeout of requests. This is the problem of scale and performance. To support growing demand, your product or system should be capable of scaling to avoid degradation of performance. Scalability is the ability of your system to meet the demand of stress caused by increased usage gracefully. Demand is expected to increase over time.

As the number of users and volume of requests grows, the system should handle the increased usage without resulting in slowness or completely grinding to a halt. Designing scalability from the beginning means that the product will be built to handle workload demands during its lifetime. The design should look at the application's scalability, service architecture, and system and geographical scale. Doing this upfront will save the need for redevelopment and maintenance overheads later on as the product grows. It will also provide a better user experience while allowing the application to enjoy greater stability.

User expectation is that software will run reliably and predictably — in other words, without failure for a sustained period. A system or service must run reliably to ensure it is highly available and can continue to perform over specified timeframes. Reliability tests include feature and performance tests. Integration and end-to-end functional tests ensure that a series of features can function as expected when executed together. Types of performance testing include load testing where the system is increasingly run under load to a point where it starts to degrade; stress testing whereby the system's stability and ability to recover gracefully is validated under conditions in which physical resources are pushed to the limit; and scalability testing which verifies the system's ability to scale, for instance by volume or number of transactions, until bottlenecks are reached.

By now, you hopefully can appreciate that quality assurance starts from the very definition of a new idea right through to the point it is safe to release it to a production environment where it can perform reliably. But it doesn't stop there because quality processes are involved in how the system can continue to be monitored and capable of detecting problems even before the user does. The ability to obtain alerts and react swiftly to resolving the situation is key to preventing downtime and degradation and to sustain a high level of customer satisfaction. Some more advanced systems are also capable of self-healing automatically on detection of an error while in operation. Essentially, the more mature an organization is with its quality practices, the more advanced it is towards optimizing its quality processes and proactively ensuring that prevention, early detection, and resolution are important factors in its end-to-end product life cycle. The effort invested in these various forms of quality will determine their success in the market and sustain their product's lifetime.

Productivity, metrics, and measures

"When will the product be released?" You must have heard this before. When you're put on the spot to provide an estimate on a deliverable feature, it can feel stressful and overwhelming—attempting to determine, with a level of accuracy, when a piece of software will be released can sometimes feel like looking through a crystal ball. Sometimes the promised date will be missed and people will be disappointed. This can lead to mistrust.

The business world revolves around annual budgets, measures, and planning to determine how to achieve targets. Unfortunately, this creates conflict and tension between the business leaders who ensure that the goals are achieved and the teams that execute against those plans. High-level plans and estimates become commitments.

Where estimates are committed without consultation with development teams, it causes unnecessary pressure and stress, resulting in delivery failures that impact quality, timescales, and morale. When teams can provide estimates, they might be challenged if there are concerns over the length or size of the estimates. This puts people under pressure to revise their estimates, and inevitably as the work begins and progresses, it leads to what will be considered delivery failures.

Estimating workload and delivery schedules can be complicated because so many variables determine the success of a project. However, it's also worth remembering that the main reason for estimating the work on a software project is to determine the project's feasibility and provide early visibility into potential risks and facilitate conversations about scope, time, and resources required to achieve a more successful outcome.

When estimating a project, the question is whether time is a useful measure of productivity. On that point, the jury's out.

In today's manufacturing industry, planning, scheduling, and optimization techniques help businesses reduce waste and production costs to determine output and delivery schedules more accurately. A typical manufacturing process involves the assembly of component parts to form sub-assemblies. The finished sub-assemblies fit into the larger final product. Productivity is measured in several different ways.

Lead time refers to when a request or demand is made when the order is fulfilled and provided to the customer. Order processing, manufacturing, labeling, and shipping are included in lead time. This includes the sub-assembly and assembly processes, which all can impact lead times.

Cycle time is the time it takes for a team to complete the production of one item, from the start to the point that the product is ready to be shipped or delivered. This time refers to production rate and is a key manufacturing KPI.

During active production, wait time measures when a task is waiting to be started or completed. When additional customizations are required to meet customer-specific needs, this extra work is likely to extend lead times.

How does this work with software? In many cases, development teams will be working iteratively on one product, evolving it through enhancements and new features. Unlike manufacturing, where many similar types of products are repeatedly produced in a factory setting, software product development typically revolves around a single product going through numerous phases of evolution during its lifetime. Estimates of work will look at how long it will take to implement a feature or enhancement of that product, and the nature of work is likely to be different from one feature or activity to the next. Ultimately, you want to bring about consistency and predictability in the delivered work, but this is harder to achieve as no two software projects are the same.

To predict the time it will take to deliver a software feature, you will need to understand how long it has taken to deliver a similar feature in the past, or you will need to break the problem down into constituent parts, each of which will allow for a better overall assessment of time to implement and deliver. The cone of uncertainty is a simple visualization tool to demonstrate how estimations work. From a high level, for instance, long before a project starts, an estimate might be carried out to present a view of work effort, size, or time with assumptions and known risks, the purpose being to share how feasible the project is and to support the approach required to drive that work forward.

If big unknowns, complexities, or risks are identified early on in the project, this is usually an indicator that a further assessment is required to demystify the scope. A proof-of-concept is a useful method for verifying the idea and as a means to de-risk the unknowns and better inform on the desired approach or whether moving ahead would be the right approach. Performing this activity close enough or during ideation and scoping reduces risk and investment in the project. It also allows teams to identify the mechanisms necessary to mitigate the risks.

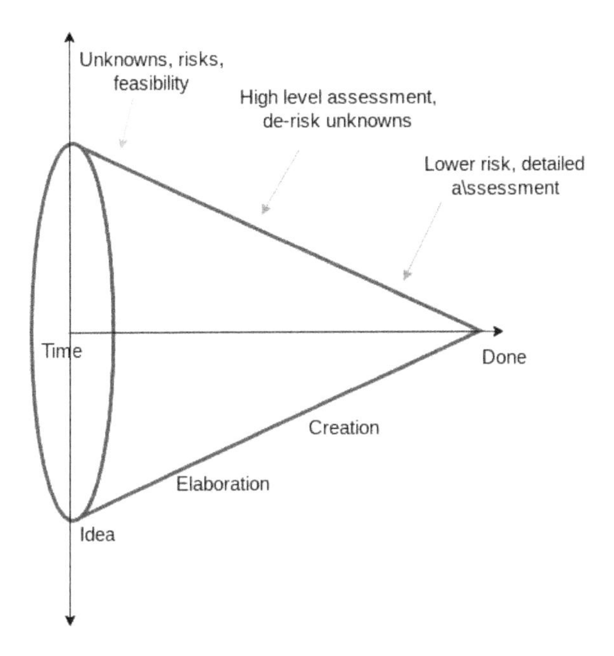

As the project proceeds, further elaboration happens with the breakdown of large topics into further technical detail, allowing the delivery teams to understand better the work required, giving them the ability to revise their estimates to a greater degree of certainty. By the time development starts, there should be a strong understanding of implementing the solution successfully, the associated risks, and a better forecast of the timeline to completion.

In Agile terms, teams use story points as a measure of effort for measuring epics and stories. A recommended method to improve these estimates is to create baselines as units of measure, which refer to the past efforts applied in delivering similar pieces of work.

During estimation ceremonies, references are made to baseline story points weighted against the epic or story being estimated. In this way, the team has a more accurate view, based on past experience, of the effort required to deliver a piece of functionality. These estimates should become more predictable in time, assuming the same team and its makeup is working on the same product. With velocity based on the number of story points that the team can achieve in each sprint cycle, it is possible to predict how many stories and epics can be achieved over several sprints. This provides a better certainty of the time it is likely to take to complete the delivery of a feature.

Story points and velocity are extremely useful tools for performing capacity planning. Understanding on average how many story points a team can deliver for each sprint, a capacity plan can be extrapolated to determine approximate timescales for delivering epics and features. As teams develop features and their velocity stabilizes, the more accurate estimates will become, and the more consistent they plan their sprints and achieve their commitments.

A more predictable development cadence requires a software architecture and system that is flexible and easily extensible, which allows teams to develop and release features more rapidly. Standardization is an important aspect of software design, as in the development of manufacturing. A set of well-defined, loosely coupled components with interfaces between them can be readily adapted and maintained. Making use of industry-standard ready-built components (instead of writing them from scratch), will save time and effort and maintenance costs. For instance, the tech industry has made improvements in defining and benchmarking standards for application programming interfaces or APIs, which enable external programmers to more seamlessly make use of the services offered by businesses, and in return, improve revenue streams for those businesses that are offering the services, as well as for the clients who can consume them to speed up their time-to-market deliveries. The question often asked is whether it is better to build or to buy the required solution.

We can measure lead time for the end-to-end delivery iteration of a feature, from requirements definition through release. During this event, we would also measure cycle and wait times. For instance, we can measure cycle time for the time it takes to complete a story or a specific coding task. Wait time here will identify the pauses between stories and tasks. Where idle time is inevitable, although this should be minimized, these can be filled with other supporting activities such as hiring or onboarding new engineers or assisting other teams with their efforts. They may be experiencing heavy workload or capacity issues. These methods can help teams identify problems and, in turn, make informed decisions quicker.

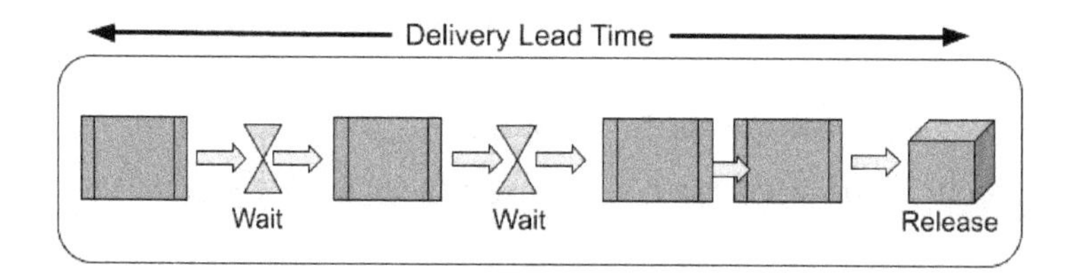

Ultimately we want to optimize how we create software products by ensuring that the teams' throughput is based on their capacity and capability to deliver consistently, in a manner that will not harm morale and to the expected quality standard.

There is no doubt that reporting is an essential tool for businesses to plan, measure and track the overall performance and health of the business. Reporting, as a powerful communication tool, is effective where it can help a business identify its progress against existing plans and identify areas for improvement and growth.

Focusing on engineering and software production, reporting can provide visibility of the organization's key operational and strategic activities. The other important expectation of reporting is to expose problems and help drive rapid improvements to keep the business on track with its plans. Business metrics share the means to measure and monitor outcomes.

In Agile teams, metrics would typically be story points, velocity, burndowns, or burn-ups. The team should own these metrics and measures to manage their work and review progress. However, attempting to report on these metrics further up in the organization can be detrimental. It will lack context and will potentially disrupt progress. Why is this?

Teams measure their progress with velocity to plan their work and understand how much they can deliver in an iteration. It also helps them determine the approximate number of iterations it will take to deliver a set of features in their backlog, based on their estimates. I have observed some businesses using (or perhaps abusing) velocity out of context to baseline all delivery teams against a particular velocity. I have even observed senior leaders challenging team estimates by judging that one team had estimated fewer story points.

Story points and velocity are relative only to the team working on a set of features. One cannot compare eight story points in team A with the same eight story points in team B and expect them to deliver the same piece of work. In fact, team A might estimate 13 story points for a story, and team B might estimate 21 points, and yet they would be capable of delivering the same story at around the same time. This would be like comparing apples with pears. The interesting measures here in comparing across teams are the cadence, consistency, and predictability abstracted from story points and velocity. Overall, are the teams consistently meeting the commitments they set in each iteration? Another reason that reporting velocity does not provide a useful organizational-level report is that there is no direct connection to desired value and impact for overall business goals.

The key here is to measure real outcomes and drive actions and behaviors to enable teams to focus on delivering the highest value solutions. Trusting teams to measure and drive their own performance to deliver against organizational goals without fear of over inspection and criticism is crucial to better productivity and higher morale, which go hand-in-hand.

A data-driven approach is desirable for teams to increase their performance when they are better equipped to understand their own productivity and identify opportunities for on-going improvement. Throughout the delivery and release cycle, teams will look at ways to depart from ad-hoc and reactive methods towards well established practices which are consistently measured, adapted, and maintained. Repeated manual steps are candidates for optimized, and in some cases, automated workflows, which in turn will reduce the burden on teams' efforts. A more predictable delivery cadence emerges, along with greater confidence as the teams develop their capability to more reliably meet the commitments they set in each iteration.

CHAPTER 6

Don't Throw an Engineer at a Problem

I'm sure some of us have come across the situation where a project is behind schedule or timeline expectations have been drastically brought forward, or perhaps a project needs to be completed at short notice. Naturally, the business will want to know why the engineers are behind or lacking in productivity, and they might suggest that more people should be thrown at the problem so that the work can go faster.

There is a misconception that the software engineer is the key and sometimes the only component to delivering a solution when they are a part of the all-important whole. I hope we can now appreciate the effort it takes to deliver a solution that requires a team and not just an individual. It is understandable if a small change in functionality is required; however, this is rarely the expectation.

The perception that software engineers are code monkeys working in a back office or sweatshop simply churning out lines of code is misplaced. Engineers are professionals who apply a qualitative approach to their work. Throwing more engineers at a problem is not necessarily going to make the process quicker. In many cases, it will only result in more problems, confusion, and delays. According to Brooks' Law, coined by Fred Brooks in his book *The Mythical Man Month,* adding manpower to a late software project makes it later. Brooks' Law states three key points in software engineering. First, it takes time for people added to a project to become productive and can also cause disruption for the existing team and the project, as they turn their efforts to helping the new people become productive during the "ramp up" time. Second, communication overhead increases as more people increase as more people will need to be kept in sync. Third, there is only so much division of tasks that can happen to keep people productive, until at some point, the overall time to complete the work decreases.

When we 'throw' people at a problem, we don't always stop to think clearly about the scope of the work. Instead, we think about the 'resources' required to do it, assuming that the engineer will figure it out and create a solution to the problem. Recently, the hero engineer was recognized and highly valued for jumping into situations to put out fires. And yet, often, this reactive approach would end up creating more fires.

The ideal setup is to prevent fires from getting started in the first place. One of the main reasons software projects fail is a lack of clarity around requirements. Poorly communicated scope will result in a poorly thought-out solution. Time estimates will be based on flawed assumptions and will likely set incorrect expectations for stakeholders. Without well-defined analysis, definitions, and assumptions based on happy paths, we miss important details. The effort required in reworking or adjusting due to scope creep could very well be substantial, resulting in significant delays, defects, and disappointment.

The best route is to have well-defined requirements, ideally defined through a collaborative approach, and ensure a more realistic assessment in delivery and resources. Software engineering requires that our software components are readable, flexible and extensible, reusable, maintainable, secure, scalable, reliable, and user friendly, to name a few. We should prevent waste and cost to the business in terms of technical debt as much as possible.

When we estimate the effort to deliver a feature and, in doing so, commit to the business, this should take account of the various activities that support the delivery effort and not just the work required to develop the code. This is one area where some projects have tended to fail. The entire team engages in estimation and planning events to ensure that they are truly accountable for their commitments to the business.

The other problem that businesses tend to create is the "pigeon-hole effect," where individuals possess separate, highly specialized domain skills and knowledge, known only to one or a few. These people become key dependencies who become indispensable and tied to their specialism. As a result, they become a high risk to the business because they are heavily relied upon. Compensating for this by paying ever higher salaries to retain the employee is a short-term strategy. In another situation, a technical specialist is promoted to a role with people management responsibilities, having proven their technical expertise as an individual contributor. In this particular case, the business 'rewards' the expert by appointing them with a role requiring a set of skills with which they had little prior experience and, in doing so, run the risk of causing disenfranchisement within their newly appointed team.

When there are many experts, there tend to be silos within a team or organization with individuals performing specialized roles with fewer interactions. For most projects, the team makeup would fare better with the core group consisting of generalists, with a smaller group of highly specialized individuals. It is important that those specialists are team members and that sharing their knowledge and expertise is built into their role. Preventing and periodically managing risk in a business is key to its continued success. As such, knowledge and experience should be recognized as risks that need to be managed accordingly. An organization that manages the flow of information will encourage a knowledge-sharing culture to distribute expertise, enable people to continue to grow, and provide more equal opportunities to professionals while recognizing and rewarding excellence. Excellence for engineers comes in many forms, including potential for growth, the desire to collaborate and influence within their teams and across the business, and deliver products to expected quality standards with productive and efficient mechanisms.

Engineers dedicate their work to a variety of tasks, ranging from high level, systems design through decomposition to manageable deliverables, coding, debugging, maintenance, and deployments for release. Each set of tasks requires context switching which can be demanding in terms of effort. It's obvious that not all engineers are the same or are motivated in the same way—some are more efficient and enjoy the challenge of designing complex solutions and breaking them down into smaller, manageable components, whereas another engineer might be happier delivering those components quicker through the delivery cycle. Helping individuals understand their strengths and how they can leverage their capabilities will improve productivity and morale in equal proportions.

One of the most powerful experiences I've had as a "techie" in my career has been in engagements with customers and external business partners. In previous organizations, as an engineer or engineering leader, I enjoyed participating in several ways, including scoping and brainstorming meetings where we came up with ideas for product innovations. I also ran forums with customers to look at proposed features, products under development, provide feedback on the roadmap and share their experiences with our products. What did I learn? That customers and partners love engaging with technology teams. They felt more connected with the business—with the people who actually built the products and solutions they used. They were more invested in discussions about how we could help them improve their experience and productivity. In turn, we understood their businesses with greater clarity and empathy, with takeaways on how we could now build even more compelling solutions that addressed their requirements. In short, this process built trust and confidence. I participated in sales processes with commercial teams to win business, knowing that we worked together as a team.

We visited as a team and presented as one organization to our prospects. And to these potential customers, they witnessed our interactions in how we represented our organization, listened and learned from them, and offered solutions to their questions, which left them feeling satisfied because the main representatives were together in the same room. We won new business through this approach. Now some business people might balk at the very idea that technologists should sit in front of customers—their concerns stem from the idea that engineers might expose too much information or make off-the-cuff promises.

On a recent visit to meet with several large customers in the United States, I was delighted to find that they made an effort to introduce their colleagues from across the business. We spent days learning about their organizations, processes, challenges, and specific requirements. It was a humbling experience—with the face of technology at their offices, they were keen to engage with us, seeking our assistance in ways to help them become more successful. Listening helped us develop a deep understanding and empathy, and naturally, we shared ready-prepared answers to some of their problems with them. At one of the offices at a well-known major tech company, by the end of the first day, they told us that *"before your visit, our customer satisfaction score was a 5. After today, it's a 9!"*.That was the power of our interaction with a key customer. We built a stronger partnership. On returning to our offices in England, we shared the customer's story with our teams and invested in delivering more valuable and meaningful solutions. As a result, our relationship with the customer strengthened, and the customer satisfaction rating remained high.

The key message here is, don't underestimate the importance of the presence and involvement of technologists in engagements within your organization and in the presence of customers.

CHAPTER 7

People, Organization, and Culture

A decisive factor for today's job-seeker is organizational culture and how well it aligns with their own values, beliefs, and principles. However, there is limited talent in our local markets within our global economy, and obtaining access to the right people with the necessary skills is crucial for a business to continue expanding in the growing technology industry where competition is rife. As technology evolves at an ever-faster pace and businesses must change with the tide, the talent pool becomes more restricted. This is where organizational culture plays an important role in attracting talent.

Culture is one of today's buzzwords in which an organization expresses its shared values, behaviors, attitudes, and characteristics in how they interact with each other, their customers, and suppliers. Culture is important in the role it plays in attracting key talent. In a market where desired skills are in high demand and competition is rife, an organization with an attractive culture will play a strong part in attracting people. This is because organizational culture is important to employees who are likely to enjoy working there and forming strong working relationships if their values and attitudes match their employer's.

Many organizations talk about diversity and inclusivity. On the surface, the idea is that they will hire more people of color and different genders. However, not much else necessarily changes when they hire more diverse people into their environment unless they take active steps to help them feel included. Without change, this can leave the new hires in an uncomfortable situation where they find they do not belong and there is a sense of tokenism. The same discriminatory attitudes are not addressed, still exist, and eventually, these people leave or remain demoralized and misrepresented.

Diversity is also part of organizational culture. An organization where everyone is welcome and treated fairly without bias has a diverse culture. I use the word "everyone" because diversity is much more than a person of color or of a different gender. These are only more visible. But there are more attributes important for hiring diversity than just these. Naming a few, they could be people of different nationalities, educational, or family backgrounds, and those with different thought mechanisms, expressions of language, and personality types. I have worked in just a handful of organizations that

I believe have managed to get this right without ever trying. They didn't set out to call themselves diverse. Instead, they hired the best people with a range of talents that would enable them to become successful. Unfortunately, not many organizations started out this way, so driving a program to attract diverse talent is important.

Let's dig a bit deeper into the subject of diversity. Imagine a place where people of different backgrounds, whether it is nationality, where they went to school, types of home environment, education, and qualifications, belong. There are also individuals with different personalities. Myers Briggs mentions sixteen different personality types. Carl Jung mentions eight types. They both refer to various types of extroversion and introversion, along with their learning and processing characteristics. Many other tests show how widely different and complex humans are.

The benefit of diversity comes into play when considering how different backgrounds or personality types might bring different approaches to thinking and problem-solving. Harvard University developmental psychologist, Howard Gardener, challenged the notion that there was one type of intelligence focused on cognitive abilities and asserts that there are eight types of intelligence. The most recognized ones are Logical-mathematical and Linguistic. The others include Interpersonal, Intrapersonal, Spatial, and Bodily-Kinesthetic. Each of these intelligences possesses valuable characteristics that allow individuals to interact and approach problem-solving in various ways.

Hiring and working with individuals requires recognizing the vast spectrum of abilities that are on offer. This provides an almost endless pool of talented candidates with various skills that can encounter problems to solve through many different perspectives. The tech industry has tended to be dominated by a narrow representative group from the population, which has meant that the industry missed out on the potential of a much broader set of talents capable of bringing significant added value for a long time. Solutions developed in the past were expressed out of this narrow range. As the diversity of talent has emerged in these businesses, new ideas and approaches have contributed to an industry that is more expansive and better equipped to serve customers across the globe. To provide equal opportunities to populations, industry and government have introduced requirements and standards that cater to diverse groups with accessibility needs, products are developed for local markets and cultures, and languages translated for customers in different countries.

Being inclusive broadly implies a culture that embraces different ideas, perspectives, experiences, and people, so that people feel a sense of belonging, acceptance, and involvement. It occurs in an environment where people can share and discuss ideas that will come from different directions. Still, each individual feels equally respected and heard through the absence of bias. People might find it challenging to accept an opinion that doesn't fit their own, and this might represent a bias in which the individual is quick to judge. The benefit of diversity is that it can open a business up to new ideas and methods to solve problems from a wider representative group, increasing their potential to approach requirements and problem solving through innovative methods.

Experience has shown that bringing together a wide talent pool has accelerated innovation. Take, for example, Kaggle, a community of data scientists and machine learning engineers who work with their peers and enter competitions to solve data science problems. Many important and successful projects have materialized from these competitions. The beauty with diverse communities such as Kaggle is their ability to apply different approaches to solving problems rapidly, providing a high rate of investment return. Hackathons are another way to bring together a group of people who can solve problems quickly and introduce new use cases, previously undiscovered. My own recent experience involved running a global hackathon where participants included colleagues from numerous countries, university students, business partners, and public members. Over 48 hours, teams across different locations came up with novel ideas which they built and subsequently demonstrated. The best ideas were awarded prizes, and we took some of the prototypes to a global summit in Chicago where we presented the solutions. This was a way to test out the innovations to a diverse audience of more than fifteen thousand attendees, many of whom were entrepreneurs, and to gauge feedback. We received widespread enthusiasm and interest in the new offerings, indicating that these solutions were suitable for product creation. The outcome was that from initiation to validation, we rapidly were able to bring together people from different walks of life and disciplines who brought new ideas and solutions that would have taken many months to uncover.

The people organizations employ, who represent the broad range of markets they serve, are likely to be key drivers for businesses in creating new opportunities, attracting a larger customer base and in return gaining greater market share, revenue, and access to talent.

Although the industry is becoming more diverse, progress is still slow. Hiring interviews, in particular technical assessments, are still, in my mind, skewed towards a narrow band of male entrants who typically design technical interview tests, modeled to some extent on how they view their own competencies and levels of intelligence, based on their approach in solving problems. These biases, conscious or not, create a barrier to entry as they will undoubtedly rule out a significant proportion of diverse candidates who may approach problem-solving in very different, yet valid methods, or those candidates with sufficient potential to learn and adapt quickly. To address this requires the elimination of bias and the introduction of fairer assessments defined by broader representative groups of interviewers. Unfortunately, not changing the model means the same types of people continue to enter technology businesses and be promoted, establishing a self-perpetuating industry lacking diversity.

Technology leaders have the potential to bring together that cultural mix of talent in an environment where people can experience their sense of belonging and in a way that inspires them to unleash their potential. Of course, this all sounds idealistic, and certainly, during my career, there have been few occasions that I have experienced such culture.

In the technology industry, a senior leader is usually someone who would have progressed their career through achievements in technical expertise and experience in people leadership. They accomplished a proven track record with promotions from senior or principal engineer roles, perhaps an architect, and eventually a people manager or executive. Proven technical experience often weighs in favor of people skills, which makes sense when required to make key technical decisions, understanding architectures, technologies, and ways of working. They must often translate complex technical concepts to a language that business stakeholders and customers can understand. Furthermore, engineering teams are more likely to respect a leader who can speak their technical language.

Proficiencies gained in a mainly technical role are insufficient to possess the capabilities required to lead people. The move from technical excellence to people management is a significant change, and just as with any new skill, leadership requires training and lots of practice to get it right. While an individual contributor in a technical role may consider mostly the notion of 'self' in their role and the impact they make through their work, people leaders consider the wider impact of their actions on people and the organization.

Rather than talk about inspirational and motivational leadership, of which books and videos are abundant, I want to focus on leadership anti-patterns to understand that it is undesirable but can be addressed to some extent through practice and coaching, training and support.

As an individual contributor, the Self-Promoter probably felt the need to gain recognition by opportunistically advertising their talents and achievements. Now in a leadership position, old habits die hard, and they continue the practice, at times taking credit for their team's achievements. In the long run, this can diminish morale in their team, and the leader loses respect. Favoritism or discrimination creates unfairness where some employees are treated better than others and can lead to low motivation and engagement. It's natural to work with people we can easily relate to, yet strong leaders will continue to maintain impartiality and fairness.

The poor listener wants to be heard first because they have important messages to share, although they tend to drown out other voices. A good leader demonstrates a willingness to listen out of respect and empathy and recognizes that everyone has an equal voice. As a result, people trust and respect them and feel encouraged to speak up. On the other hand, there is a weakness through lack of consistency or unpredictable behavior, creating stress and tension in an organization. Where problems occur, for instance, with poor performance or execution, a leader who doesn't stand with their people to acknowledge their part in any failure demonstrates a lack of integrity and accountability.

The habitual micromanager wants to exert control over the work and detail carried out by others. As a result, they become the main decision-maker and avoid delegating work for fear that it will be poorly executed according to their standards or expectations. In time, their people stop trying to exercise better judgment and lack accountability while focusing on responding to frequent demands. As people progress through their careers, seeking formal training and coaching will help them become more competent in performing their roles as leaders and creating the culture that will attract and retain a healthy workforce.

CHAPTER 8

Transition to Future Growth

Apple Inc., at the time of writing, stands as the biggest tech company with revenues in the region of $260 billion. They supply users with ground-breaking electronic goods and services. What makes them so successful? Their innovative products changed the way users interacted with devices. The company has a strong globally-recognized brand and presence that remains relevant while placing their customers at the center of everything they do. Apple has been able to master hardware and software to an exceptionally high standard of quality, with user experience being key to their winning formula.

In this book, we set out to explore the well-trodden approaches, characteristics, and patterns that have defined those industries that evolved from their infancy to prominence. Taking their learnings of the past, we have been able to identify opportunities for the tech industry to accelerate through mature practices to further growth.

People are what make businesses succeed, whether they are your customers, suppliers, or employees. Sharing common objectives and reducing silos across the business to work closely together is key to success. For example, having the customer front and center, knowing your customer, and delivering to satisfy their needs will keep them satisfied customers for life. This will also ensure that you grow market share, crucial to increasing profit and achieving market leadership.

On the theme of revenue generation, eliminating waste means that businesses save costs as productivity increases, with increased productivity contributing to frequent releases to market as teams deliver faster. This results from self-organizing teams iterating through cycles of improvement to identify better ways of working.

Successful quality standards ensure that a product or service consistently meets the needs and expectations of the market. This builds trust and brand loyalty when customers can enjoy consistently user-friendly, reliable, and resilient products. Standardized practices make more of an appearance across the tech industry, increasing productivity and improving employee morale. Beyond just practices, global standards help bring about greater collaboration, openness, and accessibility to data and technologies, along with equitable and inclusive opportunities to all participants on the global stage. These should be the real drivers to rapidly achieving widespread maturity.

The technology industry is still very much in its growth phase, with new and emerging technologies entering the market at an accelerated pace with the expectation that we will see more organizations stabilize as they mature.

Innovation is essential for businesses to stay ahead of their competition by creating or entering new markets. We are already making our way through the fourth industrial revolution, which builds on previous technologies, much like previous industrial revolutions unfolded. In this case, the automation of traditional manufacturing and industrial techniques brings together physical devices, networked systems, and big data analytics. The Internet of Things (IoT), with the multitude of electronic components and products that are entering the market almost daily, require secure practices and standards, along with robust infrastructure to enable connectivity across communities and widespread regions.

The IoT market is expected to grow to the region of twenty billion devices, generating revenue of more than one trillion dollars by 2030. The smart device ecosystem has now devised connectivity standards and a set of vendor-compliant solutions. Soon, secure devices will develop to improve the safety of IoT, leading to more widespread adoption. More use cases emerge rapidly, with early players already beginning to establish their product solutions to gain market share.

Our world is becoming more connected, not just through people, but also through 'things', and with the power of quantum computing and 5G, greater capacity and speed with more accurate real-time data capture and analytics will transform the way we live and conduct business. But it doesn't stop there. We recognize that our industries are responsible for sustainability, climate, and building a global community for the long term. This requires industry cooperation on a wider scale, with the aspiration for greater equality and fairer distribution of wealth in our diverse global population.

To be able to achieve this ambition requires businesses to move away from just short term annual horizons which today limit capacity, drive poor behaviors and centralize dominance and power for the few, towards longer term approaches which allow for building skills in place of consuming the limited talent and resources we have available today.

By evolving towards mature, established practices, the quicker the businesses will be able to move faster, deliver more quickly, and achieve a significant advantage over their competitors to accelerate their growth. Furthermore, building on a set of trusted, well-established methods leads the way for the industry to accelerate its potential to find new ways to innovate and gain market adoption, thus continuing to reinvent itself. Already, the world is heading towards a new way of life where everything and every interaction will need to become connected in a stable, secure, and sustainable way. It is worth noting that the First Industrial Revolution lasted about two hundred years, with the Second lasting around one hundred, while the Third lasted only about fifty. How long will the Fourth Industrial Revolution last?

Index

CPSIA information can be obtained
at www.ICGtesting.com
Printed in the USA
BVHW042042060921
616167BV00014B/339